LIFE BEFORE MEDICARE
Canadian Experiences

The Hospital for Sick Children's dairy, with signs in Yiddish and Italian, opened in 1909 and sold pasteurized milk and Modified Milk Mixtures as formulae to reduce infant deaths since clean milk was not generally available. Archives, The Hospital for Sick Children, Toronto

Life Before Medicare
Canadian Experiences

Compiled by Helen Heeney

Illustrated by Doug Sneyd
Edited by Susan Charters

© 1995 The Stories Project
Ontario Coalition of Senior Citizens Organizations
Printed in Canada

Life Before Medicare: Canadian Experiences
is funded by New Horizons Health Canada

The views expressed herein are solely those of the
authors and do not necessarily represent the official
policy of Health Canada.

Anecdotes contained in this volume have been edited
for length and style. The publisher is not responsible
for the opinions or facts stated by contributors.

Compiled by Helen Heeney for The Stories Project

With a foreword by Dr. Michael Rachlis

Edited by Susan Charters

Illustrated by Doug Sneyd

Book design by Justine Orr

Canadian Cataloguing in Publication Data

Heeney, Helen, 1932-
   Life before medicare: Canadian experiences

Includes bibliographical references.
ISBN 0-9699545-0-6

   1. Medical care–Canada–History–20th century–
Anecdotes. I. Title

RA418.3.C3H44 1995   362.1'0971'0904   C95-920999-9

_____

For information on obtaining copies contact:

Ontario Coalition of	or:
Senior Citizens Organizations	Helen Heeney
25 Cecil Street, 3rd floor	The Stories Project
Toronto, Ontario	RR#3 Orillia, Ontario
M5T 1N1	L3V 6H3
Phone: (416) 979- 7057	Phone: (705) 327-9079
Fax: (416) 977-9591	Fax: (705) 327-2517

To Jean Eleanor Ross Woodsworth
1913-1995

Jean believed in some ultimate intention of
justice for this earth and its destiny to be fulfilled.
She had an inner and unshakable confidence in
something beyond her own strength.

Uncounted thousands in our world, children,
mothers, women on the margins, seniors, have
been blessed through her.

Her eighty-two years are better arguments for
God than many books and sermons.

Dr. Bruce McLeod
March 12, 1995
Metropolitan United Church, Toronto, Ontario

Acknowledgments

We appreciate: the editorial skills of Susan Charters, who pulled it all together; the prolific artistic talents of Doug Sneyd and John and Justine Orr; the steadfast friendship of Jean and Larry Smith, who believed it could be done; the responsive, practical advice of Donna Kumagai, Jay Cody, Merle Larson Totten, Jim Robinson and Judy Rogers; the attentive eyes of Richard and Beatrix Robinow; the hours of patient technical assistance from Vincent Clason; the computer whizzes, Ann Billings and Karen Lloyd; and all the members of the board of The Stories Project.

This book owes its existence to the many seniors' organizations and their staffs who publicized the project and who responded with energy and care, particularly Andrew Aitkens, One Voice, the Canadian Seniors Network, and Felicia Fallen, Ontario Coalition of Senior Citizens Organizations. A New Horizons grant from Health Canada has made the national scope of this project possible. The assistance of the Public Service Alliance of Canada is also gratefully acknowledged. Kevin Sneyd, of Document Excellence, was kind enough to donate his services.

Above all, we wish to thank the contributors, without whose personal histories this composite of the Canadian medical landscape before Medicare would never have been attempted.

This book has been written in the hope that it will benefit the younger and future generations of Canadians.

TABLE OF CONTENTS

FOREWORD   i

PREFACE   v

INTRODUCTION   ix

HOME MEDICINE
    Home Remedies   1
    Doctoring   5
    Surgery at Home   9

COMMUNITY CARE
    Neighbourhood Help   17
    Community Doctors   22
    Community Coverage   32

HOSPITALS
    Getting In   39
    Hospital Routines   46
    Getting Out   54

PAYING UP
    Doctors Collecting   61
    Early Insurance   66
    Losing It All   71
    No Money, No Care   76
    Paying: The Long Haul   80

CONCLUSIONS   97

APPENDICES
    APPENDIX A:
    A Thumbnail History of Medicine   115

    APPENDIX B:
    Principles of the Canada Health Act   117

NOTES   119

REFERENCES   135

INDEX OF CONTRIBUTORS   137

FOREWORD

I was thrilled to be asked to write the foreward to *Life Before Medicare*. And, I am so thankful that the seniors of this country have taken it upon themselves to publish their memoirs of life before public health insurance. Their stories are cautionary tales for those who believe that Medicare has outlived its time. In fact, today Canada needs Medicare more than ever.

In our twentieth-century, disposable world, we have forgotten the importance of listening to the wisdom of elders. Some scientists have highlighted the significance of increasing longevity for the successful evolution of human beings. As we evolved into modern human beings, our life expectancy increased so that children could reasonably expect to have grandparents as well as parents. Before written language, these elders became the repository of a tribe's accumulated wisdom. The presence of tribal elders who knew of obscure sources of food or older hunting techniques at times of famine often spelled the difference between survival and extinction.

Unfortunately, with the exception of our first nations and a few other communities, Canadians have forgotten that our elders have important information to impart to the rest of us. As a result we face an impending disaster. More and more we hear cries that we can no longer afford Medicare. Some political and business leaders suggest that we must privatize the funding of our health care system to balance our country's books. Others are more blunt. In keeping with the developing American cult of selfishness these Canadians declare that it is their right to pay for their own care and get better service than others who cannot afford to pay the extra premium.

However, a move to private health care financing would be a double disaster for Canada. Eliminating Medicare would cause untold human misery and suffering. The eloquent letters in this volume bear testimony to the anguish suffered by many Canadians before public health insurance. While many doctors and hospitals endured financial hardship themselves rather than deny care to the sick, many patients died because no one would provide the care they desperately needed. Families were forced to make hard choices between their home or farm and care for a sick family member. And, the demeaning act of begging for needed health care not only diminished the dignity of those who were forced to plead but also the society in which they lived. Medicare has preserved the humanity of sick Canadians but it has also honoured us as a nation.

If anyone has any further question about Medicare's importance to our national character after reading *Life Before Medicare* they should investigate the American health care system. In the past fifty years, we have seen a massive social experiment in North America. Canada began to implement a system of universal, prepaid public health insurance in 1947 in Saskatchewan with hospital insurance. Canada completed its national programme of universal and medical insurance in the 1960s. At the same time, the United States rejected a universal plan and implemented public health insurance only for the elderly and the officially designated poor.

The results of this experiment are conclusively in favour of Medicare. In 1995, the U.S. has over 40 million people without any health insurance whatsoever. At least another 50 million Americans have such inadequate insurance that a major illness could lead to bankruptcy. All Canadians have coverage for basic hospital and medical care. And, the United States spends far more on health care than any other country in the world. In 1995, the U.S. will spend over 15 per cent of its economy on health care while Canada will spend approximately 9.5 per cent. Much of the difference in spending is due to the extra expense associated with administering a mainly privately financed system. There are over a thousand companies selling health insurance in the U.S. and each needs its own computer system, actuaries, and sales and marketing staff (because in the United States health insurance is a competitive business). And, increasingly, caregivers and health insurance companies find it more profitable to deny sick people needed care (for which they might not technically qualify) than to provide appropriate care efficiently.

Canada's seniors are not suggesting we leave our health care system exactly as it is now. We desperately need to reform the way we deliver health care. Up until recently, Canada focused the delivery of health services on doctors and hospitals. People waited until they were sick before contacting a doctor who then provided care in a mainly episodic fashion. We now realize that not only is this poor quality health care, it also increases costs. As the television commercial used to say – "you can pay me now or pay me later." We need to concentrate on the first level of the system, primary health care, to ensure that as few people as possible actually require more expensive institutional care. And, we know that many services can be provided more effectively and less expensively by nurses, social workers, and other health workers than by doctors. In fact, often the most effective and efficient health care is to educate patients and their families about their care or to help a patient make contact with a self-help group.

But, these reforms to the health care delivery system are totally compatible with public finance through Medicare. As a matter of fact it's easier to make these needed reforms within a publicly financed system than one which is mainly privately controlled. In Canada, democratic governments develop health policy rather than the unelected, unaccountable power-brokers who dominate the American system. This is the most important lesson the seniors have to teach the rest of us. We can solve the problems of our health care system only by working together collectively. That is how we developed Medicare over the past fifty years and that is how we will reform it for the future.

Philosopher George Santayana once said that those who cannot remember history are condemned to repeat it. Let us learn the lessons from *Life Before Medicare* and heed the call of Canada's seniors to preserve and enhance our country's most treasured social programme.

Dr. Michael Rachlis
Co-author,
Strong Medicine: How to Save Canada's Health Care System

PREFACE

It was a soft June evening in 1993 when the coffee party was held at Owl House Lane, Toronto, the home of Jean Woodsworth. As president of One Voice, the Canadian Seniors Network, Jean was introducing some of its board members to the leaders of various Ontario seniors' organizations. To the coloratura of the birds, we discussed the burning question that Jean quietly posed: "What is the most important issue seniors face today, in the nineties?"

The consensus was, the erosion of Medicare.

The Canada Health Act was born out of the socialist government in Saskatchewan, and out of the misery of the Great Depression that stretched across Canada and lasted up to the Second World War. This great piece of legislation provides for an equitable system of health care for everyone, the rich and the poor. Its erosion could end the universality and public administration of health care for which seniors have fought so hard. Jean said that we needed to begin a re-education about Medicare's reason for being.

"If only all Canadians knew about the bad old days," Jean thought aloud.

Sister Gisèle Richard, with calm clarity, offered a short, startling memory: "My mother had tuberculosis, and died after a lengthy illness when I was only eight. My dad was still paying for her hospitalization five years later, when I started taking the payments to the hospital every month."

As the discussion went slowly around the circle, my eyes returned again and again to Sister Gisèle's face, to me reflecting character and wisdom. Without a mother, this child had turned into a responsible daughter. She also helped to raise the family, and that childhood moulded the determined leader she is today, without a doubt. Depression years are indelible times. I was a Depression baby, but don't remember those times. I needed to learn.

Jean remarked that a book of stories about people's lives before Medicare could re-educate us, our families, policy-makers, and all people born since the fight for Medicare began. Although she spoke quietly, this was nonetheless clearly a directive. I thought Jean might possibly have meant me to take it on, although she didn't look at anybody in particular. I certainly felt linked to Sister Gisèle, because of her story.

The thought of compiling a book was both daunting and energizing. I felt challenged to start, at least. Being a seniors' activist had been hard work – meetings with government, and committee and consensus work – when I was co-chair of the Ontario Coalition of Senior Citizens Organizations (OCSCO). All this meant travel from our home on the outskirts of Orillia. Maybe the book project could be done from home, with fewer meetings in Toronto, and provide a way to become more involved in the Orillia community. And so it happened. Once we committed to *Life Before Medicare*, it began to grow on its own.

The first step was asking two major seniors' newsletters, those of One Voice and OCSCO, to run a call for stories about what life was like before Medicare. Fifteen letters came in to tickle my curiosity. I sought out and received some valuable advice to write a proposal to New Horizons, Health Canada, asking for grant money as the scope of the project broadened.

Then, in other provinces, seniors ran the request for stories in their provincial newsletters. Other press releases generated more stories. Two CBC Radio interviews, on Fresh Air and Morningside, were successful in encouraging a wide range of listeners to contribute stories.

Ann Billings, a recreation therapist, and Donna Kumagai, a registered nurse, and I got to work with a tape recorder in seniors' homes and club meetings. Some seniors found recognition and raised self-esteem in the experience of having their stories, recorded and typed by us, to show their relatives and friends. Many presented us with interesting personal histories and we have preserved these stories in our archives, when not appropriate for this book.

A few innocent mistakes were made, such as interrupting an important euchre game with a request for stories, and also, losing Mrs. Melnyk's address. On Morningside, Peter Gzowski called, "Mrs. Melnyk, if you're listening, send Helen your address!" But we learned from these mistakes, too. We learned that Mrs. Melnyk's doctor in Winnipeg is still alive at age ninety, and we were able to send him her recollection of his generosity.

Clearly, we were on our way when New Horizons, Health Canada funded us in the spring of 1994, and our board became active. Bea Levis, co-chair of OCSCO, along with Mary Allen-Armiento and Rita Duenisch-Turner of OCSCO, Beatrix Robinow, medical library consultant, and Jean and Larry Smith, all from Toronto, volunteered their able resources to the board. Jay Cody, Donna Kumagai, Merle Larson Totten and myself, all from Orillia, made up the other seniors required to administer the project. We are indebted to these friends committed to a common cause. Food, fun and fellowship accompanied the supportive work they contributed.

Every day when a new letter came in, the computer got busy entering data. Seniors who had a story often wanted very badly to get it across. Others had a more painful time relating the double jeopardy of illness and its resulting poverty. Jane Leitch said in a memo that accompanied her story, "This is the best that I could do. Many of the details are too difficult to write about. I can easily see why lots of people don't want to put their stories on paper. It brings back some memories we have put out of our minds. That was yesterday! Thank God we survived. Thank God for our present coverage. May it long continue." And George Baigent vehemently states that, "It is not just the paying of bills that one must deal with, but rather the depressing feelings one gets as the efforts to go forward have you in a position of losing ground or, at best, just treading water." Each letter brought encouraging words of support to us and exhorted us to keep on telling "how it was."

Community caring in the days before Medicare is well marked by the contributors to this volume. The hub of community caring was often the physician, the first provider of universal coverage, usually not charging those who could not pay, and treating everyone fairly. Many accounts of doctors' faithful service explain why some doctors deserved the pedestal older persons reserve for them even now.

But the long haul of paying for illness and death for many years was also a reality in those days. More heart-rending still are the stories of those who couldn't begin to even think of paying, and so did not seek out any medical care.

Throughout the process, the project has created interest because the subject matter is compelling. The average Canadian cherishes the system of health care we have, and many seniors recognized their opportunity to contribute.

Telling their stories validates life as it shaped the Canadian landscape. That this life was hard and unkind, bittersweet and funny comes out in the everyday family occurrences described by the contributors. Personal diaries, pictures and family archives have been ransacked to find these records, to give us a clearer identity and fiercer pride in just who we are. We Canadians are marked by our universal Medicare programme, and this is shown in these stories of our roots, roots of adversity without universal health care.

Hardship can be instructive. Days of struggle and toil to pay off debts did not go unnoticed by the children whose mother took in laundry from the summer tourists. They admired their mother's "strong back and resolute wit," as well as her independence.

However, the stories in this book make it clear that life without Medicare was vastly different from the life we know now. Do we want that colder, harder life back?

Helen Heeney
Orillia, 1995

INTRODUCTION

In 1994, the late Jean Woodsworth, to whom this book is dedicated, recalled:

The Depression years were the years of my growing up on an apple farm near a small village in eastern Ontario.

Living in the country meant you knew the joys, pains and sorrows of your neighbours and community. In those years, many were in very difficult circumstances. I was also deeply impressed by my father's donation of truckloads of apples to the Toronto unemployed.

The cost of medical care was one of the most painful situations many people faced. Proud and needy people visited the one doctor available only in times of extremity. Recently, I heard that during these years, one-half of Canadians never in all their lives received any medical attention. That seems a very high percentage to me, but perhaps that is because the doctor in our community was caring and very hardworking. Many patients paid him in chickens, eggs, potatoes or apples. Some were unable to make any payment. It was a situation which was devastating for both patient and doctor. The patient had to beg for medical attention for himself and loved ones. The doctor must have been overstocked with food articles beyond the needs of his family, but without the ready cash for taxes, car upkeep, or clothing for his family.

In the 1940s, Canadians and their governments recognized that the caring acts of individuals for their neighbours were not sufficient for those in need, and constituted a ridiculously backward system for a modern state. The plans for what we now call our "safety net" were put in place to cover every Canadian during the necessities that face all of us: illness, unemployment, and the burdens of childrearing and old age.

That safety net has not only made us self-respecting and proud citizens, but it has served to bind us together as a country. We have the knowledge that no matter where we may travel or work in the whole wide nation, the safety net will support us.

Today, there are threats to our health care system, to unemployment insurance, to our old age security benefits, to child care. In fact, there has already been serious erosion of each of these parts of the social safety net.

Those of us who remember the bad old days have a duty to make known, to our governments, the disaster that faces our people and our country if we let slip those programmes which grew from the suffering and distress of those Depression years. We must insist that Canada continue to be one of the best countries in the world in which to live. We want the progress of our lifetime to continue for our children and our grandchildren, and for every Canadian. It is unthinkable that we should return to health services which are not universally accessible and available.

The Canada Health Act is the centrepiece of that social safety net which Jean Woodsworth speaks about. Although the Liberal party platform promised a public health insurance plan back in 1919, it took the government of Saskatchewan, in 1962, led by Premier Tommy Douglas, to first accomplish it. The National Medical Care Insurance Act in 1966 spread the programme across Canada, each province entering separately over several years. The five principles of the act – universality, accessibility, comprehensiveness, portability and public administration – were the basis of the Canada Health Act of 1984. Under both pieces of legislation, the federal government shares the cost of Medicare with the provinces. The federal money acts as a carrot to provinces to get them to apply the principles of the act, and when the act is breached, the money can be withheld, the offending province being smacked smartly with a stick.

There have been of course, powerful stakeholders who oppose Medicare. Doctors went on strike in Saskatchewan in 1962 to fight the Douglas plan, and Ontario doctors struck in 1983 over the right to extra-bill. Bargaining with these opponents has given us fee-for-service coverage and a "sickness industry" that looks after us when we are unwell. As well, Canadians today spend, on average, $400 a year on prescription and over-the-counter drugs, and seniors account for most of this. "Seniors are being drugged silly," in the words of Dr. Dennis Psutka of McMaster University, addressing the Senior Citizens Consumer Alliance for Long Term Care Reform for Ontario in March 1992.

There is more to health than simply dealing with sickness. Perhaps we are ready for a balance of wellness and illness, a belief in some of our own powers to heal ourselves. Tommy Douglas foresaw that public health care should emphasize the prevention of illness and promotion of health. Our health care system has not yet caught up with his vision.

Right now, Medicare is being eroded, instead of improved. We face an increase in private insurance services and user fees. Drugs are costing more, and the use of expensive technology is increasing. Provincial funds are being stretched. Every province suffers different symptoms from medical cutbacks. Soon there may be one system for the rich, another for the poor.

Economically, we can continue to have a universal, comprehensive, portable, accessible system, but only if we preserve public administration, and strongly curtail the huge insurance conglomerate. The Canada Health Act provides the vision for the provinces and all health care providers and consumers to follow.

As grandparents and seniors, we see that the health of our grandchildren depends not only on Medicare, but on other determinants such as nutrition, employment, education, environment, housing and income. Child poverty is rising rapidly in Canada as unemployment hovers around ten per cent and higher in many regions. When times are tough, grandparents often assist financially and provide stability both for their children and grandchildren. Seniors have a substantial stake in the future, and don't want to see the hardships of the past revisited on the generations to come.

Warnings describe the demise of Medicare as we have known it. Born out of compassion, perhaps being killed by stealth through policies driven by economics, the universal principles of the Canada Health Act are treasures Canadians need to defend vigorously. This book mirrors the values of this great country, moulded from the rocks of adversity, by the long haul of paying off debts, and by the wisdom and experience of its elders.

HOME MEDICINE

Health care in Canada in this century began
with what you could do for yourself at
home. When physicians were scarce, you
relied on patent medicines and home cures.
You doctored yourself at home, sewing
cuts, nursing family members, or relying on
wise women or midwives. When available,
doctors came to the house as a matter of
course, if necessary performing surgery on
dining room and kitchen tables by the light
of oil lamps.

Home Remedies

The homesteaders' medicine chest contained dry mustard, Epsom salts and aspirin. The Epsom salts were used to clean wounds of man and animals too, the dry mustard was used for mustard plasters on the chest and of course, the aspirin was used to cure everything else.

Birgit Ethier – Medstead, Saskatchewan

It was the year 1911 in the Peace River country, Alberta. Settlers were leaving Edmonton by horse team, ox team and their own two feet in an effort to get a homestead and/or a script (320 acres purchased). A man could get 480 acres and his wife could do the same. In total they could get one and a half square miles of land, much of it wide open prairie.

They struggled over about five to six hundred miles of rocks, mudholes and bush trails. Needless to say most if not all were quite young or in their best years. They brought their own home health care with them. I know of only one doctor in this land rush and I think he only practised for a short time. For the most part these people healed themselves. The first hospitals were run by church missionaries. After a while a health nurse was available and needless to say much overworked.

About 1915 my younger brother died of dysentery. The doctor had to leave on a fifty-mile trip to treat a sick woman so mother had no other help. One time later she told me that if she had had the patent medicine Castoria she could have saved him. Dr. Higbey roamed over about three

Dr. Higbey roamed over three thousand square miles

thousand square miles. Medicines were not very effective in those days in Grande Prairie, Alberta.

Actually, health before Medicare was a wild animal's portion.

Arthur W. Fletcher – Hythe, Alberta

Rawleigh's Products were used. Salesmen covered their areas in summer by horse or horse and buggy. Among other items they sold red and white liniments, which were very potent. The white was used for rubbing on the throat for colds, etc., and the red was mixed with water and a little sugar; it was drunk to fight congestion. Carbolic salve was used in many ways and for many purposes, for humans, cattle, and horses. When livestock suffered barbed wire cuts, carbolic salve was the answer.

I remember many home remedies my parents relied on, for example: "For hoarseness of the throat, take milk and red pepper every little while." On the lighter side, there was one farmer, Mr. Hoffman, whose remedy was, "Mix home brew with Epsom salts. After a few doses you might still have the cold, but you won't notice it!"

A lot of home remedies were published in a book called *The People's Library* by R.C. Barnum. Co., Toronto, in 1917.[1] It gave advice on every kind of ailment including "Grandpa's Heart Disease." The book was dedicated "To the People," captioned "May it Serve Them Well in Their Hour of Need."

The list was endless. It was generally believed that if the treatment failed, it was the Lord's will to take that person to rest.

Jacob Holst – Delta, British Columbia

My mother was very young when she married and took on the responsibility of a home consisting of herself, my father and my elderly grandfather. She often told us of the time my grandfather was very ill with pneumonia and she nursed him back to health with bags of salt which she heated, wrapped up, and placed around him in his bed, being careful to arrange the hot bags of salt before removing the ones that had cooled off.

One of the most painful experiences I have ever had was when I was a schoolgirl and I got an infection in my face. This was so bad it swelled until my lip burst. My only treatment was boracic acid, which eased the pain somewhat.

Emily MacPhee – Perth, Ontario

Medical treatment in those days was simple: bread and milk poultices, salt and warm water to draw out poisons and infections from the body, mustard poultices for inflammation, as well as herbal remedies. Alcohol was used to wash wounds and taken internally to relieve pain when available.

V. Foster-Clampitt – Langley, British Columbia

Treatment for the Poor. Archives, The Hospital for Sick Children

Mother would never ask for help.

Father died when we were ages five, seven and ten years of age. Mom cleaned houses for $1 a day in the thirties. My brother had convulsions in the mornings, so Mom took him to Sick Kids' Hospital[2] by streetcar one day for some medication.

The rest of us got paregoric and syrup for colds. We were dewormed every spring with Stedman's Worm Powder. We had castor oil regularly and enemas to "make sure your system is cleaned out."

Audrey Ross – Orillia, Ontario

I once knew a family who told me their little boy had whooping cough when he was an infant. This happened during winter in a house in the country where their only source of heat was a wood stove. The family took turns holding the baby day and night for five weeks. When one tired, another took over the task until he recovered.

Emily MacPhee – Perth, Ontario

Most of the babies were born at home, with the help of a midwife or a good neighbour. I have known of several cases where the fathers had to deliver their own babies, there was no other help.

One man set his own broken nose with two sticks inserted into his nostrils and pressed out the broken bone. His only remark was, "It made tears come to my eyes."

It made tears come to my eyes

Another cured ringworm with axle grease and used blueing, used for whitening clothes, on stings. Whipped egg white would cure the stomach flu and strong tea, cold of course, would help a sunburn, when washed on the infected part.

Birgit Ethier – Medstead, Saskatchewan

Doctoring

In Saskatchewan, we lived in the area between Herbert and Gravelbourg, some twenty-four miles from Herbert and some thirty miles from Gravelbourg. Very few farmers' wives had the opportunity to have their children born in hospital. Distances were too great and transportation by horse too slow. In serious situations where surgery was required, I recall Dr. Sovey driving the patient in his buggy or sleigh over the rough roads to Gravelbourg. Ambulances were unheard of in those years. Most children in the area were delivered by midwives. There were one or two who had nursing training or experience, but apparently it was not until Tommy Douglas that some midwives were given training.[3] Farmers' wives looked to midwives for help, only turning to doctors in very serious cases.

She heated drinking glasses and attached them to the stomach

An incident vivid in my memory is of my younger sister, Merceda, trying to climb up into the wagon while it was being pulled by two horses. Somehow she got under the wagon, one of the wheels going over part of her abdomen. The midwife was called. It was fascinating. She heated drinking glasses, attached them to the stomach, drawing the skin up into the glasses. Surprisingly, after several weeks in bed, my sister survived.

Jacob Holst – Delta, British Columbia

The boy who could "see the meat" is fourth from the left, front row

About fifty years ago I was teaching in a little country schoolhouse in Salem, Nova Scotia. One morning one of my little students came to share with me his personal "Show and Tell." He held out his little hand that was covered with a dirty, bloody bandage which he pulled aside to show me his injury. Excitedly, he told me, "You can see the meat!" He had been cutting the kindling wood for the stove when the hatchet slipped and sliced his hand open at the base of the thumb. You could indeed "see the meat." I phoned the school nurse and explained the situation. She said, "The roads are in such poor condition, I can't possibly get through the mud to get there. Even if I could, I wouldn't dare touch it. He needs a doctor."

That was out of the question, but I couldn't leave him in that condition, so I got a basin of water and washed his hand, diluted some iodine so it wouldn't sting so much, and put a clean bandage on. It should have had stitches, but it healed anyway.

Emily MacPhee – Perth, Ontario

The church was having a fall supper and had no facilities in those days, so the boiler of hot water had to go to the church. It was November, and my brother and another teenager were loading the boiler when he just happened to slip off the edge of the wagon and the boiling water came down on his leg.

It was very hectic nursing him at home. The doctor came to the house, of course, but my brother was delirious, and had to have constant attention. One day my mother had to get something done, and told me to sit with him. It was scary!

"Sit on the chair, and if you need me, you call me." I did, and soon!

My mother, of course, dressed the wound, and I remember particularly one day as my mother started to take the bandages off, all the meat on the leg came with it. He eventually healed, but wore a shin pad for a long time.

Emma Shellswell – Coulson, Ontario

This happened when the party-line telephone was out and the roads bad, and when I say bad I mean very bad, with the "gumbo" mud of northern Alberta. (It could be used to chink the cracks in the old log cabins, one of which we lived in for fifteen years. That is how sticky and strong it was.)

This unfortunate day was one that will live always in my memory. My husband came in from the barn where he had been caring for the cows and he looked entirely unlike himself. He is not a heavy man and usually in good health because he doesn't drink or smoke but this day he had a blue tinge to his complexion. In the middle of speaking to me he suddenly fell to the floor choking and clutching his throat. He was trying to say to get help, which I was trying to do. The phone, as I said, was out, no neighbour near to help. I couldn't get out. So what could we do? The attack did not last very long but afterwards we got him up and settled him in a chair; he found that easier than flat down in bed. When he felt better he got up and went back to work. What else can a farmer do?

For many nights he had to sit up in a chair to sleep and when we finally managed to get to a doctor he said regretfully, "It's too late to say what caused this. Could have been indigestion." They didn't have all the machines in the country then even if we had the money to pay.

Betty Peters – Abbotsford, British Columbia

Surgery at Home

The doctor proceeded to hand-drill through the skull

It was around 1921 or 1922. My father's dad was in an auto collision between Teviotdale and Harriston, Ontario – side-swiped, overturned in the ditch, and suffered some severe skull/brain trauma. He was removed from the accident site and taken to their home in Listowel. Doctor was summoned and the dining room was eventually turned into an operating theatre. Excess fluid pressure in the skull had to be relieved. My dad's mother's assignment was the cloth/boiling water needs. My dad's was "to hold the light."

I recall my dad saying that the doctor said to him words to the effect, "This isn't going to be pleasant. Do you think you can do the job? Once I start I have to have the light till I'm done." The doctor then proceeded to hand-drill through the skull in an attempt to remove the excess fluid and relieve pressure.

The operation was to be unsuccessful and his dad died some days later, not regaining consciousness from the time of the accident.

Why wasn't his father taken to a hospital? Maybe there was none very close, maybe my family couldn't afford it. Maybe the doctor felt that the remedy could be done just as effectively at home as at a hospital, at less cost. It's hard for me to believe: to be an attendant to an operation, performed in my own home on a close family member, at the age of fifteen or sixteen, and then to see it all for naught, anyhow.

John Hallman – Oro, Ontario

TORONTO STAR, MAY 14, 1933

LAD OPERATED ON MOTHER WHEN DOCTOR DIDN'T COME

Used razor to make incision and woman showed improvement

Sudbury, Ont. When a doctor from Sudbury refused to visit her at her home in the country, six miles from Sudbury, without payment of $10 in advance, Mrs. Mike Smeegie had her 12-year-old son, Steve, operate on her for pleurisy. With a razor Steve made an incision in his mother's back and drained off more than a quart of fluid.

Provincial police, learning from a neighbour of the amateur surgery, visited Mrs. Smeegie to find her condition improved.

Today, however, her brother, Sam Manchula, is in Sudbury looking for a doctor willing to treat Mrs. Smeegie without payment in advance, for, he said, she had taken a turn for the worse. As a last resort he is appealing to District Relief Officer W. J. Laforest.[4]

Mike Smeegie, the woman's husband, was recently sentenced to six months in Burwash Industrial Farm for a breach of the Excise Act, and his wife and young son were left alone on the farm.

An Element of Luck

Dr. E. A. Gray, Medical Superintendent of the Toronto General Hospital, said today there may have been an element of luck, but it was possible young Steve Smeegie had carried out an operation on his mother at their farm home near Sudbury as stated. Dr. Gray said the boy had probably made an incision between the ribs, somewhat after the manner a physician would adopt by use of a surgical needle for such purposes.

Contributed by John Bohman – Weston, Ontario
Reprinted with permission, Toronto Star Syndicate

Our farm was in the Rumney Settlement, Somerville Township, two and a half miles north of Coboconk, Ontario.

As was customary, my brother Logan and his friend Orval made a weekly pilgrimage to Coby (short for Coboconk) to collect the mail and in Logan's case, to get tobacco for our dad, Ben, also. On one such a trek, on foot, they successfully brought home the mail, tobacco, and the friendly germs of scarlet fever. Both lads' families were stricken with the dreaded malady. In our home our mother, Rachel, not to be outdone, came down with it also, as well as her three children, Logan, Lauretta, and I, Beulah. We were quarantined, of course, with the emblem of notification on the front door. Having had the disease as a child on Blue Mountain, our father, Ben, was immune to it. One of his sisters had lost her hearing due to the malady.

My sister Lauretta developed a very painful swollen gland on one side of her throat. She required assistance to stand up or lie down. At the same time, I suffered from an earache, which appeared to be improving. When the ear drained freely, my parents weren't too concerned. The pain had subsided and all seemed well.

Rachel and Ben Richmond with children Beulah, Logan and Lauretta

Unfortunately, the pain returned. Time went on, and fortunately an elderly neighbour, Mr. J. S. Rumney, called to see how we were getting along. The scarlet fever scare kept folks away. When he saw my swollen head, he was horrified, and urged my father to get the doctor. Until then my parents hadn't realized the seriousness of the affliction, but with a head shaped like a teakettle on the left side, and due to the neighbour's concern, they began to realize their daughter, aged ten years, was seriously ill with mastoiditis.[5] My father went to Coby and explained to the local doctor, Dr. Robert Ingram, the situation. Dr. Ingram called at our house every day for some time, driving his horse and cutter, with my father stabling his horse each time. It was late December 1923, and early January 1924, and there were no antibiotics, sulpha drugs, or penicillin in those days. The only medication the patient received (which I loathed, yuck) was Milk of Magnesia! When the condition worsened, syringing with a healing solution of some kind day and night was to no avail.

At last came the morning when Dr. Ingram decided he could do nothing more to help the situation. He advised my mother to tell her husband to not go cutting wood that day, and for her to not leave my bedroom. (But, as she had a multitude of things to do, she tried to get some cleaning done.)

In the meantime, Dr. Ingram had notified Dr. N.D. Buchanan, eye, ear and nose and throat specialist, Peterborough, Ontario, and he was to come to Coboconk by train, which he did. Next day, Dr. Robert Ingram drove Dr. Buchanan up to our settlement. The previous night, I had suffered some sort of crisis, which my mother had witnessed. I remember wondering why she looked so shocked!

The next evening, Dr. Ingram and Dr. Buchanan arrived via the trusty horse and cutter. They

He had time to grasp the lamp as Mr. Fielder toppled to the floor

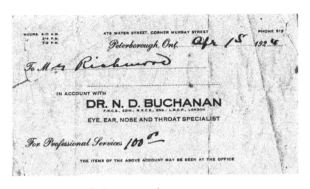

The invoice my father received

proceeded to set up an operating room in our big draughty kitchen, which had the world's worst stove for supplying heat. I recall my father carrying me downstairs, and I was astonished to note that Dr. Buchanan was putting on a nightshirt – or so I thought! Then I was surprised to see Orval's parents were present. (Mr. and Mrs. A. W. Fielder's family had had the scarlet fever, as we did.) I was laid on the big kitchen table. Dr. Ingram proceeded to administer chloroform (yuck) to the patient, saying, "Do you like the smell of that? Take a deep breath." I fought like a tigress. From then on I missed all the excitement and activities. Mr. Fielder was given the coal-oil lamp to hold (no hydro of course). Dr. Ingram noticed the light was wavering and he had time to grasp the lamp as Mr. Fielder toppled to the floor. He had fainted and remained on the floor as the surgery continued, without further incident.

Having scarlet fever in the house and due to the fact there was not an isolation ward in Ross Memorial Hospital, Lindsay,[6] at that time, it was necessary to have the surgery take place at our home.

I'll never forget it!

I have in my possession the invoice my father received from Dr. N.D. Buchanan, eye, ear, nose and throat specialist, Peterborough, for $100, dated April 15, 1924, to Mr. Richmond. Also, I have a receipt from Robert Ingram, M.D., dated May 3, 1924, in the amount of $111.50, re: professional visits, assisting with operation, etc.

For some years afterwards, my surgery and recovery was a great feather in Dr. Ingram's cap. Who could blame him?

Beulah M. Barr – Hillsdale, Ontario

COMMUNITY CARE

The community has always been a provider of health care. Neighbours helped with nursing care, creditors and relatives supported families paying off medical bills, and public health nursing brought care to many neighbourhoods. Community-based doctors often cared for patients with no thought of financial return, and are lovingly remembered. However, from very early on, Canadians found more structured ways of providing community coverage, turning to payroll deductions, community-run insurance plans or municipal levies to ease the burden of health care costs.

Neighbourhood Help

Every morning she walked and nursed our neighbour

I recall the winter of 1932. January was very cold and stormy. The temperature would hover between thirty-five and forty-five degrees below zero. That's when my mother took it upon herself to nurse our neighbour who lived a mile away. So every morning she walked and nursed our neighbour with mustard plasters and hot chicken soup. This kept on for three weeks. There was no thought of going to the hospital, because there was no money.

Birgit Ethier – Medstead, Saskatchewan

I came from a small town in Manitoba, an area where community members pitched in to help sick townspeople. I was in my early teens when my sole parent, my mother, fell ill. I don't remember how long she was ill, but I do remember ladies being at the house to help.

I remember the chill when one of them told me, "Your mother has a rupture of the abdomen, and she'll have to have an operation."

I didn't know what a rupture meant, but I'd seen one on an animal and I knew what happened to the animal. I also knew that there was no money for an operation. I think my mother wore some special clothing to help or ease the rupture. I know she never had the operation. I never spoke to my mother about such things. I don't know what kind of pain she was in. I know I lived in constant fear that she would get sick again. No trip to the hospital ever happened. The town doctor came, and I don't know if he was ever paid.

What I remember about that time was the fear. I feel the feeling now, as I write. Someone dear was ill, and the chance of getting an operation was as good as the chance of flying to the moon.

Betty Osborne – Toronto, Ontario

The year was 1926 and Mother had just given birth to twins, Anna and Lawrence. Despite the fact that Mother already had four children, they were managing. Daddy was an extremely hard worker and with the caring concern of a large extended family, they coped very well for that time.

However, before Anna was a year old, one eye had to be removed in the hope that she would have permanent sight in the other. She was fitted with an artificial eye and everything seemed fine till she was about six years old and had started to school. Then started a slow decline. The sight started to diminish and she underwent treatments every six weeks. This went on till she was ten years old, when she died.

How did my parents cope with the financial burden that these long-term treatments presented? I don't know. However, I do know that our landlord, the grocer, the doctor, and even the company that supplied fuel, supported my parents by allowing bills to go unpaid, or at least by accepting token payments. Their attitude was, "When you have the money, we will receive payment in full." And they did.

Peggy Snider – Ardtrea, Ontario

I would like to tell how two brothers helped their sister in a medical emergency in the 1930s.

The two brothers were my dad, Joseph Holinaty, and his brother, Michael Holinaty, who lived with their families on neighbouring farms, several miles from Wakaw, Saskatchewan. Their sister, Theofilia Adamowski, lived with her family in the small town of Wakaw. Theofilia became widowed in 1934 when

Theofilia made the eighty-mile trip home in a 1932 Model A Ford

her husband, Mike, sought medical help in Rochester, Minnesota, where he unfortunately passed away. Because of their poor financial situation, his remains could not be returned to Wakaw and he was buried in Rochester.

Two years later, in the summer of 1936, Theofilia required emergency gall bladder surgery. This would be done in a Saskatoon hospital. However, there would be no surgery and no hospital care unless there was a guarantee of payment previous to the hospitalization. No guarantee, no surgery. It was as simple as that. And her brothers were not going to put that to the test!

Joseph and Michael signed a guarantee for payment of $400. The surgery was successful, and after a week's stay in the hospital, Theofilia made the eighty-mile trip home in a 1932 Model A Ford over a dirt and gravel road. Her brothers and widowed mother accompanied her home.

How did they earn $400? There was a lot of wood cut, sawed and delivered to people. Cord wood brought in $2 a cord, and firewood brought in $1.65 for a pole load.[7]

Elizabeth Holinaty – Edmonton, Alberta

I was born in 1911. My parents were farmers in the Interlake district in Manitoba. In 1919 all our family became sick when the flu epidemic spread like a vapour through the land.[8] Medical bills were hardly paid before typhoid fever spread to our home. The doctor ordered a nurse from Winnipeg and placed us under quarantine, and if it had not been for neighbours helping us financially and with work on the farm we would not have survived.

Stefania Morris – White Rock, British Columbia

I can find no photos, snapshots, no visual record of my family during the Depression, pre-Medicare years. I think it was a time of such stress (polio, Alzheimer's, the loss of my niece through a doctor's indifference and negligence) that one had neither the inclination nor the strength to record the exhausting struggle.

My mother started a garden after my father's death from Alzheimer's. We had been totally ostracized and estranged during the years of his illness. No one visited us, there was no relief, no in-house care was available. Hospitalization was out of the question, and there was no Alzheimer's Society.[9] One coped alone.

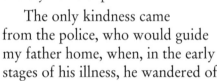

The only kindness came from the police, who would guide my father home, when, in the early stages of his illness, he wandered off in search of his childhood farm. Different from the people of the nearby church, who, when my father wandered in and sat down in a pew at the back to rest, phoned us and demanded immediate removal of such an inacceptability.

The only kindness came from the police, who would guide my father home

B. L. Williamson – Ottawa, Ontario

When I was pregnant with my first, and later with my second child, I did not visit the doctor until I was five months pregnant. The first fee of $40 took us about two years to pay off. The family doctor allowed us to pay it as we were able. When the second child arrived, the fee was slightly higher, but it was the same arrangement. At that time we didn't have a hospitalization plan either, so the hospital, delivery and nursery charges were approximately $50. We were able to pay that a bit at a time, over two years.

At that time they had, here in Winnipeg, well-baby clinics[10] that were attended in our area one day per month. The care of an infant and/or young children was basically advised and adjusted by them. There was an M.D. plus registered nurses. If anything serious developed, you were sent to a practising physician.

Ruth Mayor – Winnipeg, Manitoba

In 1951 I started in public health. I worked in the east end of Toronto. The residents there were mostly young married working class. I found public health meaningful for me as they were open to our visits and appreciated our help and teaching.

I had as clients a family with three children living in a basement apartment which was damp, cramped and not healthy for children. Their youngest child, about one year old, had a heart problem and required admission to the Hospital for Sick Children frequently for pneumonia. This family was trapped in this living situation because of the expense of caring for this child. The father worked two jobs trying to get ahead. There came a time that the Hospital for Sick Children would no longer admit the girl until the bill was paid. They had to try different hospitals that they didn't owe money to.

As a public health nurse I felt powerless to help them. We tried to get community agencies to help. We did get glasses for one child but it was a band-aid approach.

We did get glasses for one child but it was a band-aid approach

Marea Lemke – Etobicoke, Ontario

Community Doctors

There was the annual picnic at Rob Roy School on July 1, 1912. Father walked there from his homestead over five miles, to tell me to come as soon as possible with the team and democrat, as his neighbour, George Hall, was in critical condition. Mr. Hall would have to be taken to the doctor in his bed, as he couldn't walk.

I drove on to Dad's homestead, had dinner, and with his help we carried the mattress with the patient to the democrat. Mrs. Hall came along. It took us till supper time to get to Dr. Hayunga's homestead, mostly across prairie. I angled right to the Hayunga log house through his crop to the kitchen door. Supper was on the table. Mrs. Hayunga had started to pour the tea. I stepped inside quickly and said that the man was a stranger to me, and he had no money, but he needed attention immediately to save his life, and I was prepared to pay the doctor for the work.

We carried the mattress with the patient to the democrat

He said to bring him in, but I said he couldn't walk and we'd have to take the mattress and man together. We got him in the front room, and doc told me to tie my team, as he might need me. Mrs. Hayunga had hot water and cloths, and I stayed in the kitchen when I wasn't needed. I smelled disinfectant very strongly. Finally the doctor came out and told me to put up my team and have supper. He said I was fortunate to get the patient there alive. He had to cut into him four inches and take out a quart of pus. The sac was at the bursting point.

I had supper Saturday evening and Sunday evening and Dr. and Mrs. Hayunga took care of Mr. and Mrs. Hall. I took them

❀ ✿ ❀ ✿ ❀ ✿ ❀ ✿

home after supper Sunday. Doc wouldn't take anything off me; he said he was paid. On the way home George Hall said I saved his life.

Mrs. Hall was sent $15 to buy a cow. Mr. Hall gave this to the doctor, but he only took $2. Mr. Hall said they were the best-hearted couple he ever saw.

E. F. Owens – Lucky Lake, Saskatchewan
Contributed by Dorothy Owens Larson – Peterborough, Ontario

My father was a physician practising from 1922 until his death in 1970. The care of the sick was his first priority, and in the Depression years often there was no pay. In many instances pay was in kind: a quarter of beef, half a pig, hay, oats, stove and furnace wood, etc. I can think of many instances when in stormy, cold winters, long trips were made to the sick who were penniless.

A woman in Ottawa told me this story. Her father, John, had five or six children and fell ill with acute appendicitis. My father went to their farm eight miles away. As soon as he saw John he diagnosed the problem, and said he would have to have an operation as soon as possible. It was winter, before roads were ploughed. They were seven miles from the railway station, where next day there would be a train to Ottawa for the hospital.

John said he could not go. He had no money. The Ottawa surgeon had to be paid up front. After an hour of pleading, John agreed. My father assured him money would be waiting with the Canadian Pacific Railways agent next morning. When John was taken by sleigh to the station, $100 was there.

As I recall, the same John used to come to our place, often with a load of wood on his sleigh or a few bags of oats or a roast of beef. Never did I hear anything said, but I expect over time the $100 was all paid.

William E. McDowell – Shawville, Quebec

I was about twenty-five, I would guess, about 1925. There were three of us logging in a swamp north of Brechin, Ontario, and we went there with sleighs and one horse drawing it. We used this horse to skid the trees out with.

This evening the boss called and said it was time to go home, and I had a tree partly chopped down. But it was right near a wide, deep ditch and I was afraid to leave it partly cut down for fear it would blow across the ditch and then there would be a lot of trouble. So I thought that I would work fast and get it down. At those times everything was dear, and this man got the blacksmith to draw his

They were all afternoon sewing my foot up

axes out instead of buying new ones. The frost was in the timber and you'd strike the frozen timber and some of it came flying, with the axe. And that was what happened to me. The axe came back and hit my foot, very near cut it right off.

So I had to call the lad that was next to me and tell him. Then he yelled to the boss, and they took me to Brechin. It was between two and three miles in the wintertime, in the cold, on the sleigh. So the doctor said I'd have to go to the hospital when I got there, and I said I didn't want to go to the hospital, couldn't afford it. So he said, well, he knew some place where I could stay in Brechin and he'd see me oftener and see how I was doing.

So I found a place with a couple where I could stay. His wife gave me an anaesthetic the next day, and they were all afternoon sewing my foot up.

I paid the doctor so much a month, working out afterwards. He never chased me for it at all. I got it paid without any trouble. It took a while but he didn't mind.

Howard Eastcott – Orillia, Ontario

I came down with pleurisy and Dr. Patchell in Elmvale, Ontario, was called, taking the time to drive our winter roads seven miles to see me. He was sitting by my bed with a cup of tea and a generous plate of cookies which my good wife was wont to serve. After chucking a needle in me, he asked, "What about your wife? Kind of down?"

"Yes, of course, me sick and no money coming in."

That day, before he left, he said, "Come in next week, and bring your sample books. We need our hall re-done, and my wife can pick out a pattern while I am looking after you."

Well, I papered their hallway upstairs and down, and when it came time to settle up, the good doctor's wife said, "Mel, the doctor said to pay you the full amount."

"No," said I. "Just pay me for the paper, and take the rest off my account with the doctor." And after some talking, that was that.

M. A. Boyce – Saint Catharines, Ontario

We lived in Kirkland Lake, Ontario, in the early forties and my mother was very ill. Dr. Rumball said she must have a hysterectomy, no ifs, ands, or buts about it. We had no money. My dad was furious. My mother was in tears for days. My mother went next door and phoned the doctor's office and said we just couldn't afford it. The doctor phoned my Dad at work and said that this was a life and death situation and not to worry about paying.

To make a long story short, the hysterectomy was performed the next day. Mom came home about a week later with her stitches in and was to return to have them removed. About the second day home, Mom said there seemed to be something wrong with the incision. We removed the bandage-binding to take a look. Mom's incision wasn't healing; the stitches hadn't held. I ran next door to the service station and phoned the doctor. He said, "I'll be right there."

He was there in about two minutes. He took the bottom sheet

on the bed and put it on Mom like a diaper, picked her up and we put her in his car. Back in the hospital, Mom was stitched up again with a different type of stitching.

We never did get a bill. Mom lived to be ninety-one.

Katherine Morrison – North Bay, Ontario

When I was ten years old, we lived on a small farm outside of Palgrave, Ontario. I come from a family of four boys, one sister and myself, the oldest daughter.

We had all six been to visit the doctor's office. I loved to go and see him. Dr. Noble was a tall, grey-haired man with a kindly face, and he talked so gently, a real country doctor. Dr. No was our pet name for him.

After he checked all six of us, I remember he spoke to my Mom and Dad behind closed doors. We were listening outside, hearing phrases like, "cheaper by the half dozen...get it all over at once...." I remember Dad saying, "I don't know where I'll get the money, but go ahead and make the arrangements."

Out from the doctor's office came Mom and Dad and Dr. No. Why was Dad looking so glum, and Mom, who always had a reassuring smile for us? "Oh, it's okay," I remember thinking, "Dr. No is laughing." But as they all came and sat down with us I realized, "Oh, oh. This is different."

Dad explained that four of us had to have our tonsils out so they might as well do all six of us and get it over with. Boy, I wish I'd had a camera when I think of all five faces I looked at that day.

Dad said that because it was going to cost a lot of money to have all of us to the hospital, this operation would take place at home. Somehow that seemed to reassure all of us. And we started making plans for what we would do while at home recovering.

Right here and now, I must say that Mom, all five feet of her, must have been a saint. On a Thursday morning in 1950, on the kitchen table, we all had our tonsils removed in the following order: Bunny, ten years, Bill, nine years, Danny, seven years,

Michael, three years, Carol, five years, and Jimmy, two years. Dr. No and his grim nurse and my Mom and Dad were in attendance.

I remember waking up in my Mom and Dad's bed. Beside me was my sister, Carol, and the youngest, Jimmy. Dad was at the side of the bed sitting in a chair. The kindly Dr. No started telling me how brave we all had been. Brave? Hell! We were petrified.

Brave? Hell! We were petrified

What a ten days we had at home – tears, laughter – oh, oh, all over. Time to go back to school.

In later years I asked my parents how in the world they ever paid the doctor's bill. Dad smiled. "Those were the days," he said. He had called Dr. No several times and asked him to send the bill so they could start paying on it monthly as they had agreed to do. Finally about three months later, an envelope from the doctor's office arrived.

The bill read: "Thanks for the pleasure of being the doctor to a wonderful Dad and Mom, with six cherubs God calls children. My bill to you is, keep up the good work. No charge. Dr. Noble, Palgrave, Ontario."

Bunny Kusey – Orillia, Ontario

It was my great good fortune that our family moved to a jewel of a town called Blind River, Ontario, on the north shore of Lake Huron. Dr. Hamill was our local G.P. and his office waiting room was the porch of his house and the examining room was squeezed somewhere between the kitchen and living room, as near as I could tell from the furniture I spied when the connecting door was ajar.

As youngsters we were constantly up to something that involved an element of danger, which led to our share of cuts, bruises and minor fractures. Without so much as a thought we would limp, crawl or be driven to Dr. Hamill's little waiting room. After treating each patient he would size up the gathering crowd of customers and select the one in worst need of treatment, or on a first-come, first-served basis if no obvious signs of trauma were evident in his porch. (Of course he had no secretary/nurse.)

The good news part is that the good doctor knew who had money and who didn't (we didn't) by our appearance or just general knowledge of the townspeople. I'm not certain how many cuts I've had sewn, and small casts plastered on (hockey in the winter and God knows what in the summer), and even a tooth pulled when the dentist was out of town and I was in pain, but we never received a bill, and no questions were asked. We'd get a hug or a pat on the back and be sent on our way. He frequently treated people in their homes if they had difficulty getting to town, including birthing babies and treating the elderly.

He was a saint of a man with a sympathetic and compassionate nature and practised medicine as a humanitarian calling.

Ray Garvey – Vancouver, British Columbia

I was born in 1938 and my father was a family doctor in Westport, Ontario, about fifty miles from Kingston. Our father's office was attached to our house. Probably when I was around three to four years of age, my father took me on rounds with him. That meant I got to travel around the countryside as he made home visits in the morning. Sometimes I was invited into the homes. Many people were happy to see a youngster.

Once I remember my father asking me if I would like to see a newborn baby. We went into a small house. All I remember is a kitchen and then the bedroom with a big double bed. A woman was resting in bed and there was no sign of a baby. But when Dad asked the mother if she would like to show me the baby, she reached under the covers and produced the infant. My Dad checked the baby over and then turned to the father, who was quietly sitting in the kitchen. "You have a strong, healthy baby here," my Dad said. I remember how modest or embarrassed the father seemed, as he remained speechless. My father had attended the delivery of this baby the day before. He would often spend hours in a home to be present for the birth. He took wooden blocks to place under the bedposts to alleviate strain to his back. He was saddened when the medical profession decided that safe deliveries could be determined only in hospitals. Then he drove his patients to the hospital in Kingston and had long waits at the hospital. Gone were the days of a friendly environment for home deliveries!

My father practised during the dirty thirties and the war years. During these times, he often received payment with a cord of wood, the Christmas turkey, and other produce such as poultry, eggs and whipping cream. My mother used to make wonderful ice cream with the whipping cream. My mother played a special role besides caring for the household. She answered the phone and the office doorbell when Dad was out making calls. Some patients grew to like my mother so much that they would purposely come to the office when my Dad was out. They were assured of a friendly chat with my mother and often that was all they needed.

My father would call down from his bedroom window

I never saw anyone being turned away because they couldn't pay. My father tried to have office hours in the afternoon, leaving the morning for house calls and the evenings for office visits or some relaxation. The doors to his office and to our home were never locked. His bedroom window looked down over the office door. Often in the middle of the night the doorbell would ring. My father would call down from his bedroom window, that the door was open and he would be there in just a minute.

Mary Gradnitzer – Quesnel, British Columbia

My husband was a brand new M.D., a private in the Royal Canadian Army Medical Corps. We lived in a basement apartment that cost over half of our $90-a-month income. He came out of the army a captain and set up a general practice in small-town Ontario.

Very few people had medical insurance, and very few people could pay medical bills except seasonally. Most were fishermen or farmers. An office call was $2 and a hospital call or house call was $3. Complete prenatal and delivery was $25.

At the end of eight years we had over $20,000 in unpaid bills on the books. We had made many friends, had accepted many parsnips, smelts, and homemade articles as gifts in lieu of payment. We brought up five children on hamburg, oatmeal, and love.

When Physicians Services Inc. and Associated Medical Services[11] and other insurance companies were developed our income increased, but a small-town family doctor was never rich – in money.

Nobody paid in December or January, and our Christmases were usually slim. When we had little food we used our wedding-gift china and ate in the dining room.

Emma Gordon – A small town, Ontario

My father, who served as a stretcher bearer in the First World War, graduated from medicine in 1922 at the age of thirty-two. He and my mother settled in a village in southern Ontario where he was the second doctor, and served a rural area and small hamlets within a fifteen-mile radius. My father was on call twenty-four hours a day, seven days a week. He took the occasional Sunday off, and one week of holidays. To my knowledge, my father never turned a patient away. He drove miles, even at night, whether the patients had paid their bills or not.

He struggled to get pensions for veterans, and regularly appeared at council meetings begging for relief for some of his patients. My mother used to say that, if he antagonized anyone, it was people who might possibly pay his bills. He was paid with cords of wood and farm produce, and once a child of ten turned up to pile wood to pay for his own birth. He dispensed drugs, since the nearest pharmacy was

Once a child of ten turned up to pile wood to pay for his own birth

fifteen miles away, and many of the drugs were dispensed at no charge. He argued that, if he wanted his patients to take the medication, he had to supply it.

My father had been brought up on a farm, and had a bountiful garden, and raised chickens as a hobby, so we ate well. My mother sewed, so the two of us were dressed well. My father rejoined the army in 1940, and at that time he wrote off $10,000 of unpaid debts. He re-established his practice in 1946, with some difficulty, and retired in 1963 after my mother's death, when he wrote off another $10,000 in unpaid debts. These do not sound like large amounts, now, but they were then.

Ann Elson – Picton, Ontario

Community Coverage

Newfoundland differs from other provinces mainly because we were a British colony until joining Canada in 1949 and our development has more or less followed that of the Old Country.

In 1935 a cottage hospital system (based on the existing one in the Scottish Highlands) was established here. This was the first instance in North America of a government-established, and subsidized, hospital and medical care plan set up on a prepayment basis. Costs to individuals were $5 to $7 per year or $15 per family. Again, in 1935, the government established a medical service on the southwest coast of the province with the operation of the M.V. Anderson as a hospital ship. In 1947 the Commission of Government purchased a boat and converted it into a floating clinic, known as the Christmas Seal, that provided x-rays and general health education to the outport residents.

Margaret MacDonald – Kilbride, Newfoundland

From about 1893 or 1894, in the towns of Sandon and New Denver, West Kootenay district of British Columbia, a hospital was built by the miners' union, and a doctor was employed to treat miners who were sick or had an accident. The union member had to pay the hospital and of course the doctor $1 a month. This entitled him to health care. In 1897, Slocan City[12] also had a hospital and employed a doctor. The mine owners did not pay anything towards the doctor or the hospital. These towns were booming in the 1890s and into the 1900s. By approximately 1908, this system of health care had disappeared along with the large population of mining people.[13]

I.L. Cooper – Armstrong, British Columbia

The small hospital overflowed, and tents and stretchers were pressed into use for hundreds of patients. Photo: The Cobalt Daily Nugget

My mother, Mary Jackson, from Woodstock, Ontario, was a 1907 grad of Toronto General Hospital.[14] She was attracted by a call for nurses at Cobalt, Ontario. A small frame hospital was built there to care for the many prospectors that flocked there after the discovery of silver.

Unsatisfactory sanitary conditions resulted in a disastrous outbreak of typhoid. The small hospital overflowed, and tents and stretchers were pressed into use for hundreds of patients.[15]

My mother was nurse in charge, and dealt with the most primitive work conditions.

Wilma McCann – Orillia, Ontario

I'm a retired Cape Breton coal miner. I went to work in the coal mines after I returned from overseas military service. The reason I went to work in the coal mines is because I have never found a better lifestyle than is offered here and it was the only employment offered here. During my mine employment we, and my father before me, had a system of Medicare long before Tommy Douglas even thought of it.[16] Every week we had a deduction from our pay. In my time it was twenty cents for the doctor, and twenty-five cents for the hospital. They called it "check off." This allowed us and our families to receive free medical care from our doctors and the hospitals. I, and my family, and my father's family, have been in the hospital many times and there was no extra cost to us because of the check off. We even made the check-off payment to the hospital after Medicare came in to pay for extras, such as private rooms and better meals.

Regardless of what people think, the Cape Breton miners had Medicare long before Tommy Douglas. I think it started in the twenties.

Tony Troicuk – Glace Bay, Nova Scotia

A bunch of people in the Pontiac organized the Pontiac Co-operative Medical Services and that helped a great deal.[17] We paid an annual fee into the fund and each year we'd elect a board to administer it, paying out medical expenses to people who needed it. It was just an insurance company, but we ran it ourselves and everyone volunteered their time and talents to make it work.

I think there may have been lots of these co-ops in the rural areas. It was a sort of an offshoot of the Farm Forums that emanated from Macdonald College when it was an agricultural college, very forward looking.

Rosaleen Dickson – Carleton Place, Ontario

In 1917 the Saskatchewan Legislature passed an act that was popularly (but not legally) known as the Matt Anderson Act, named for the reeve of a rural community north of Regina. As you might guess, Anderson was a Scandinavian, and drawing on his background entered the fray in Saskatchewan on behalf of publicly sponsored and provided medical care programmes. Initially, this act authorized municipal governments to levy local rates and enter into contracts for the provision of general practitioner services. Under this act, a number of Saskatchewan municipalities, mostly rural, undertook the provision of medical services. As I recall, at a somewhat later date the principles of the act were extended to enable local governments to enter into contracts for the provision of specialist services.[18]

The programme developed continuously until World War II,

eventually providing coverage for something like 150,000 persons, a substantial proportion of the province's rural population. The scheme was particularly popular in the depression years, providing guarantees of some level of service to those covered, and some level of compensation to participating doctors. At the end of the war, with increasing prosperity to say nothing of increasing public discussion of socialized medicine at both provincial and federal levels, the programme lost most of its lustre for the medical profession and dwindled to ultimate extinction.

Thomas H. McLeod – Ottawa, Ontario

A freak accident filled my eyes with potassium permanganate crystals

In 1946 my wife and I bought a home in a tiny village called Brock, Saskatchewan. There was no doctor within twenty-two miles and only a tiny drug store. The village and municipality councillors came up with a wonderful idea. A small tax was added to all properties and was used to hire a young, single doctor. A guaranteed wage was promised and payments to Kindersley Hospital.[19] Our new doctor was a real God-send. He saved my eyesight when a freak accident filled my eyes with potassium permanganate crystals. He spent hours removing them, plus the skin off my eyes. When he heard I was moving to British Columbia he insisted I have my tonsils removed which had bothered me for four years in the army. It was all paid for by our council.

This was one of the best deals I've heard of. Our good doctor earned a fair wage and didn't have to worry about collecting bills and we had the peace of mind that goes with a bit of health security.

Robert G. Haine – Cranbrook, British Columbia

HOSPITALS

Visits to hospitals were put off as long as possible. An understanding physician might waive his fee, but hospital administrators collected. Getting in could be a problem, since some hospitals refused admittance without prior payment, regardless of the emergency. Hospital routines varied, as did their facilities. Hospitals collected blood and charged patients for it. Some classified patients according to their ability to pay, and for those who could not pay, they billed the city, which collected from the patient. Once in, it wasn't always easy to get out. Some hospitals refused to discharge patients until they paid in full.

Getting In

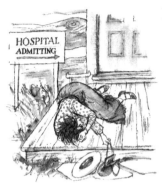

*One mother died on
the hospital steps*

By 1920 or 1925 Grande Prairie had the luxury of two doctors and some nurses. It was trying to replace its log hospital with a better building.[20] The biggest difficulty with the hospital was that payment for the bill had to be made before the patient was admitted. If you had no money available you had better stay home. One mother died on the hospital steps while her husband was at a desk pleading to have her admitted.

Arthur W. Fletcher – Hythe, Alberta

In 1935, a neighbour harvesting with a combine with a faulty design was struck on the head with the levelling lever. It opened up a hole in his skull. For three days he lay in a coma. Finally he was taken eighty miles to Saskatoon City Hospital.[21] Before they would admit him his wife was grilled as to how many chickens, cows, pigs, horses, etc., they owned, what income from eggs, cream, and on, and on, all this while the husband was unconscious. After surgery and installing a silver plate, he recovered. These people were honest, paying the final instalment on the bill with interest five years later.

Geoffrey A. Hopkins – Saskatoon, Saskatchewan

When my father was a young man, he worked in the mines in Sudbury, Ontario. He injured his arm somehow and it became infected. His arm was swollen and he even had a fever. The nuns at Saint Joseph's hospital[22] refused to treat him because he owned no property in town. He walked back to his boarding house and his landlord walked back to the hospital with him. Then he was treated.

Lillian Laakso – Ottawa, Ontario

As a teenager, my uncle used to help at the general store and deliver goods by horse buggy. This was in Amos, Quebec, in the late thirties. My grandfather was a school inspector and had left Papineauville, Quebec, for the north in the late twenties to open the first government-sponsored French schools.

One day my uncle was making a delivery when the buggy untied itself from the horses and he found himself pulled from the buggy and thrown on the ground, the buggy passing over his left arm, shattering it in two places.

My uncle was taken right away to the Catholic-run hospital,[23] where my uncle was told that he could not be helped until he paid $100. He obviously did not have the money on him and attempts were made to contact my grandfather right away, but he and grandmother were in town shopping and were nowhere to be found. My father was called instead. He did not have the money either, and proceeded to head to town to a man's clothing store where he hoped to get credit. He obtained the $100 this way, and headed to the hospital. Meanwhile the family doctor had heard of the accident and found my father. He was deeply offended by the nuns' attitude and told my father not to mention that he had secured the money.

As they walked in the hospital again, they were confronted with the request that $100 be paid to secure treatment. The doctor intervened and told the nun that he would take care of the treatment for free. My uncle was taken to surgery for free that day, thanks to the intervention of the country doctor, who never claimed payment for this intervention, as for many.

Please understand that my grandfather was a devout Catholic who believed in contributing his time and energy to support the church. He not only inspected the little country schools but also taught nurses-to-be at the local Catholic-run hospital, for free. This was, therefore, not a case of religious or cultural discrimination, but simply a typical case.

Josée Gabrielle Lavoie – Shellbrook, Saskatchewan

In 1940 a young man with a wife and two children became very ill. The local doctor said that he must go to Saskatoon City Hospital. After a great deal of persuasion the rural municipality agreed to guarantee $50 for admission. After ten days in hospital he returned home to recuperate. The bill was finally paid in 1943.

Geoffrey A. Hopkins – Saskatoon, Saskatchewan

The Cobalt Hospital and ambulance, around 1910. Photo: The Cobalt Daily Nugget

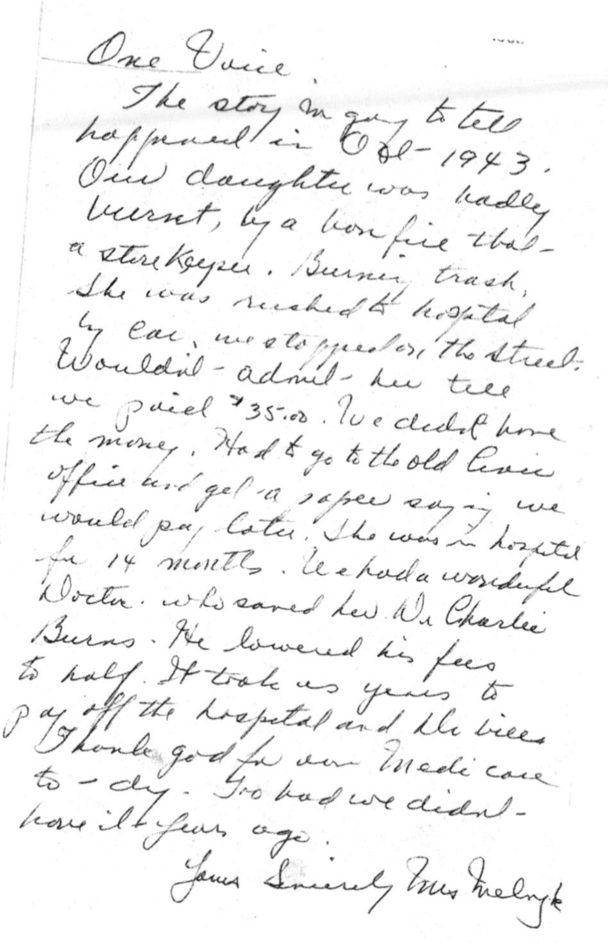

One Voice

[handwritten letter reproduced in print below]

The story I'm going to tell happened in October 1943. Our daughter was badly burned by a bonfire that a storekeeper, burning trash, had built. She was rushed to hospital by a car we stopped on the street. They wouldn't admit her till we paid $35. We didn't have the money. Had to go to the old Civic Office and get a paper saying we would pay later.[24] She was in hospital for fourteen months. We had a wonderful doctor who saved her, Dr. Charlie Burns. He lowered his fees to half. It took us years to pay off the hospital and the doctor bills.

Mrs. Melnyk – Winnipeg, Manitoba

In June 1945, I was expecting my first, and as it happened, my only baby. The European War had just ended but my husband's commanding officer did not think the birth of a baby sufficient reason to give an airman leave to travel from the east coast to Ontario. When it seemed essential to hurry to the hospital, I presented myself at the reception desk of the General Hospital in Simcoe, Ontario.[25] I was asked why my husband wasn't with me.

"He couldn't get leave."

"He doesn't live here?"

"No, he is serving with the armed forces."

"Are you married?"

"Yes, on July 7, 1942."

"Do you have your marriage certificate?"

"No, I never thought it was necessary."

"Well then, you will have to pay in advance for your hospital stay."

"Why?"

"Because you are a transient."

I have long since forgotten giving birth, but I have never forgotten being told I was a transient. One of the meanings of transient in the Concise Oxford dictionary is, "a temporary visitor." But I had lived and worked in this town for over four years, my parents lived here, I had been married here, and my husband was away through no choice of his own. I was clutching the counter with white knuckles by this time, and I sometimes wonder what would have happened had I not been able to write out a cheque for the full amount.

A rather amusing footnote to this story is that the doctor was "at dinner" and although called would not be disturbed. My sister, an R.N. visiting me from Saint Thomas, Ontario, delivered my healthy seven-pound daughter. Neither the hospital nor the doctor offered to give me even a partial refund, although my sister was soundly lectured about providing services in a hospital other than her home hospital.

Jacqueline Morris Reimer – Stittsville, Ontario

May 4, 1946, I married my soldier-boy sweetheart, who had just returned from four and a half years overseas, and was working in the Collingwood, Ontario, shipyards.

It came time for me to go in hospital to have my first baby in 1947. My mother had helped deliver many babies around Collingwood, but my doctor told her I was to have my baby in hospital, and not at home.

The hospital asked my husband for payment in advance, which was $35 for delivery, and $10 for complications. My roommate, the mayor's son's wife, was not asked for advance payment.

Jean Lester – Napanee, Ontario

My parents are immigrants from Ukraine. During the war, we believe around 1942, my mother was taken seriously ill. It turned out to be a kidney stone. They had no doctor, but neighbours, etc., rounded one up. He told my parents she had to go to hospital immediately; since he was not affiliated with one he put her into a cab. My parents went to the Royal Victoria Hospital, a

Hospital staff would not let her in until she produced $75

teaching hospital in Montreal.[26] Hospital staff would not let her in until she produced $75. This was a great deal of money in the forties and not easily at hand. My father called the woman my mother happened to be cleaning house for at the time. This woman was a wealthy, well-known Jewish woman who called her doctor, called the hospital, etc., and insisted on my mother being taken in. It was only through her kind and forceful intervention that my mother was accepted immediately.

Genia Lorentowicz – Toronto, Ontario

In the fifties, my father had a kidney stone attack. I'm told that is an excruciating pain, worse than childbirth (though that part, I may be skeptical about). An ambulance came and took my father, writhing on the stretcher, to the Ottawa Civic Hospital.[27] On arrival, they demanded that my father give a cheque and he had to fill one out, writhing, on the spot, before they admitted him.

Nadia A. Senyk – Ottawa, Ontario

When my mother was forty-nine or fifty, either in 1958 or 1959, she was a ladies' garment worker and belonged to a union, and as such had some form of insurance. At 7:30 a.m., as she was crossing the street in front of her home, on a miserable, rainy morning, she was struck by a car. The ambulance took her to Maisonneuve Hospital.[28] They took x-rays, found she had a fractured pelvis among other injuries, and left her in the hallway. It was only after 5:00 p.m. that day that they told her friends she could have a bed if they paid $100 up front. They went scrambling around for the money. My aunt told me that the banks were closed at 3:00 p.m. in those days, and that was a lot of money to have in the house so she went from door to door gathering up the money. My mother did have a doctor, who was reached and arranged for her transfer to another hospital. The insurance card hadn't helped to admit her; she was left in the corridor, filthy dirty, as she says, all day long after a serious accident. So serious that she was in the hospital for weeks after that.

Genia Lorentowicz – Toronto, Ontario

Hospital Routines

My grandfather ran a rural coal mine in the Orkney district which is about twenty miles from Drumheller and twenty-seven miles from Trochu, Alberta. My grandparents, Harry and Annie Jane Trentham, had five boys and one daughter. In the 1930s if you were a municipal ratepayer in Drumheller, a hospital visit would cost you $1 per day; if you were not, it would cost $4 per day. However, a non-municipal ratepayer could purchase insurance for $10 per year which would then bring the cost down to the equivalent of the municipal ratepayer's cost of $1 per day. A visit to Trochu hospital cost $2.50 per day.[29] Although Trochu had a very qualified nursing staff – the Sisters of Charity, Our Lady of Evron looked after the nursing – the one doctor they had would predominantly deliver babies and treat minor illnesses in the rural area.

Times were tough in the thirties and my grandfather had decided the family could not afford the $10 insurance premium; if anyone became sick they would go to Trochu for $2.50 a day. If you worked on a farm then, as my uncles did, you might expect to make $30 per month in the summer and if you were lucky enough to work in the winter you might make $10 a month. In June of 1938 my grandfather came down with typhoid; he decided the family couldn't afford the Trochu hospital and after five weeks at home and a couple of visits from the doctor, he died. Five weeks in the Trochu hospital would have cost him almost $90. Drumheller would have been around $140.

The oldest son, Fred, came down with typhoid in late August, followed by his sister

The family sent Fred (right) to Trochu because it cost less money

Marjorie almost immediately. The family sent Fred to Trochu because it cost less money. Marj was nursed at home by a neighbour. Fred had been sick for a week at home before going to

the Trochu hospital. After ten days in the hospital he died. Marjorie recovered. A blood transfusion was one way to combat the disease, although it was quite new at that time. Trochu did not have the blood supply or the technology to carry out blood transfusions. Drumheller did. My father firmly believes his oldest brother, Fred, would never have died had he been in the Drumheller hospital.

After Fred had died, my grandmother paid the $10 insurance premium. She had always been very uncomfortable with the decision to let the insurance premium slip. In the fall of 1938 my grandmother and

She had always been very uncomfortable with the decision to let the insurance premium slip

two more sons, Harold and Frank, along with a neighbour, were all in the Drumheller hospital for a month with typhoid. They all recovered.

Carriers of typhoid never knew they carried the disease. In this case the carrier, new to the area, was not discovered until after the disease ravaged the district. Seven out of eight in my father's family caught the disease; two out of seven died. The oldest son, Fred, would have certainly made it had he been admitted to the Drumheller hospital. Perhaps my grandfather would have made it too.

If you had money or a company insurance plan you had access to the treatment you needed. If you didn't, you were in trouble.

Rod Trentham – Red Deer, Alberta

I was born in 1930 on a farm twenty miles north of Regina. My sister was born eighteen months later. My parents were on a rented farm. It seemed we went from one medical crisis to another as one year followed the other.

My mother had asthma. The only treatment was either a good stiff drink of whisky or a few days in hospital. As mother was very definitely anti-alcohol, this treatment was not used. If the attacks got too bad, a shot of adrenaline was the usual treatment. It was the trips to hospital that were an adventure.

More than once my parents were turned away from the Regina General Hospital[30] because they could not guarantee the hospital bill would be paid. The owner of their farm lived in Regina, and father would have to get him to co-sign a paper stating the bill would be paid. Eventually the bills did get paid, how I will never know. Then my parents would be billed again. I suppose conditions were desperate with the hospital finances and an accountant would be given the job of trying to collect twice.

Fortunately, my parents had a tin-covered steamer trunk that was kept locked. Every receipt they ever got found its way into that trunk. They never did have to pay any bills twice, but there sure were many desperate searches through the disorganized trunk.

Robert L. Pittendrigh – Regina, Saskatchewan

In 1942 my mother was diagnosed with cancer of the larynx. There was only one doctor in Canada who could do the necessary surgery and he was in Toronto.

We lived on a farm about 120 miles southwest of Saskatoon, Saskatchewan, and like most of the farmers at that time we were poverty stricken. You could hardly imagine what an immense problem it was to undertake that trip.

My poor father borrowed money from our local storekeeper and my mother, very much underweight, hardly able to speak and able to eat only soft foods, made the long, tiring journey by train to Toronto. I was working in the civil service in Ottawa so I left my job and arrived in Toronto just five minutes before her train came in. I was able to get a small job at Simpson's to enable me to stay near the hospital. We knew no one so we were on our own.

The hospital could not accept her back as a patient until the bill was paid

She had her surgery on May 23, 1942. Her larynx was removed and she of course was no longer able to speak. She was in hospital for four months. When I took her to stay in a rooming house for a month before we left for home, the hospital told me they "could not accept her back as a patient until the bill was paid." Can you visualize the anxiety I went through trying to care for her and keep my job, not to mention her terrible suffering?

She was in and out of a Saskatoon hospital for almost a year before she died on August 9, 1943, at the age of fifty-seven.

That poor dear woman lay in her bed trying to communicate by notes. She was very worried about my two younger sisters' educational possibilities. One of her last communiqués read, "My insurance may cover some of the expense."

Betty Hopkins – Saskatoon, Saskatchewan

In 1944 to 1947, while attending Saskatchewan University,[31] during the summer holidays I worked in the admitting and discharge office in Saint Paul's Hospital.[32] Before Medicare, blood transfusion donors had to be found and the patient had to pay $10 per pint of matching blood.[33]

One patient with pernicious anaemia required transfusions frequently. A relative paid a sum which was kept on account at the hospital. On holiday weekends donors were in short supply. Hospital employees according to hospital rules could not donate blood.

One July first, Dominion Day, I was working. Try as we could, a donor was not to be found. And there was no money in safekeeping. Without blood the patient's life was threatened. Since my blood was his type I was asked to donate. I was back at university for several months when the patient expired and I was paid for my pint of blood.

Frances Berscheid – Calgary, Alberta

In 1962 prior to giving birth to our first child, the Queen Elizabeth Hospital[34] informed us that there might be an expense to anticipate for blood transfusions. In order to avoid receiving a bill, it was suggested that I find two donors, which I did. But had I not found my donors, well… The gynaecologist also had his bill waiting for us.

Our priority at the time of planning a budget was not how to feed the kids, but how to pay for the medical care during and after pregnancy.

Thelma Cadieux – Pierrefonds, Quebec

I trained as a nurse in a large, modern city-owned hospital in the years 1936-1939. The hospital was designed to provide service for those who had money and for the less fortunate.

Patients with money would be admitted to private and semi-private wards while those who could afford to pay a small amount and those who were classed as indigent were admitted to public wards. These public wards were crowded, often with hardly enough room to move between beds.

Public ward patients were, and were expected to be, the focus for medical and nursing education students.

Patients in private and semi-private wards were cared for by their own doctors; patients in public wards by the doctor assigned to them on admission and by student doctors, who like nurses, were in learning situations.

In return for the privilege of being able to admit private patients to the hospital and use operating rooms and other facilities, physicians were required to provide three months per year (according to their specialty) to patients in public wards.

Patients in private and semi-private wards when discharged from hospital would go to their doctors' offices for follow-up.

Patients in the public wards were referred to the appropriate clinic conducted by the outpatient department of the hospital. They would be given a return date and the inpatient chart would be directed to the outpatient department where they would in all likelihood be seen by a different physician from the one who cared for them in the hospital. This doctor, too, would be a specialist in the area and would be assisted by student doctors.

As with wards, clinics were crowded and persons would often have to wait for long periods "lined-up" to be examined by medical personnel. Tremendous indignity was often associated with this experience.

Service to public patients allowed little or no opportunity to develop a trusting relationship with a physician. Contact with long-term nursing staff provided almost the only continuity of contact.

A two-tiered system of health care is based in part on the premise that individuals can obtain insurance against catastrophic illness. This is not necessarily so. Once a person develops a condition requiring care, insurance coverage is cancelled. This was prevalent prior to Medicare days.

Hazel Wilson – Edmonton, Alberta
Reprinted from Alberta Council on Aging News,
March/April 1995, at the request of the author

Clinics were crowded and persons would often have to wait for long periods.
Archives, The Hospital for Sick Children

I was in training in a large city hospital from 1944 to 1947. We were the ones who paid the price due to lack of Medicare, also interns. The hours were long and education was mostly by experience with little theory to back it up. I fell asleep every time I sat down after finishing. Patients who couldn't pay were just billed to City Order (CO)[35] and they were well cared for. If we broke thermometers or boiled baby-bottle nipples to extinction CO was billed. We got the idea that the city was very benevolent. Unfortunately we weren't aware of the fact that the city exerted undue pressure on these people for payment. I felt for the patients who had some money but not a lot. We had to take them to accounting before they were discharged to make arrangements for payment. This was of real concern. The rich were billed extra to pay for the poor.

Marea Lemke – Toronto, Ontario.

When I went to work at the Cancer Institute I was employed as a social worker in the department of Social Services and Admitting. I later became director of the department. We had to assess each patient's social and financial situation in the light of the medical diagnosis and prognosis. Our assessments were reviewed by the administrator but rarely questioned. The medical or administrative staff or our own department could initiate a review as time passed or the medical, financial, or social situation changed.

We were able to classify patients as: Pay; Arrange Instalment Payments; Hold Account, for a specified time; Bill Estate; Bill Estate on death of spouse; Bill Insurance, with all the above categories for the remainder that the insurance didn't cover, or No Pay for the remainder. We could also classify patients as No Pay for any services.

Mildred Cleverley Holst – Delta, British Columbia

I was a resident in the forties in paediatric medicine. It was sometimes difficult to admit patients to hospital when necessary. Usually we asked if they could afford it, because we knew that financial help from the city to pay the bill was at that time quite punitive. One simply could lose the house or car, or whatever one owned, to the city.

The first medical insurance was OMSIP,[36] and that freed us up a lot. We generally did not bill those who were poor for physicians' services.

Vivian Abbott – Rowanwood, Ontario

In the sixties I worked on a large medical ward at Saint Michael's Hospital in downtown Toronto.[37]

Many patients could not afford insurance coverage, and as a result would lose their precious savings. Many couldn't afford to see a doctor or pay for the medications they needed.

As a result of this, many patients were extremely ill when admitted. Sometimes it was too late to help them, and even when they improved they could not afford to continue with some of the medications they needed to sustain them.

The hospital would even give a free week's supply of medications. We would often see patients readmitted.

Louise James – Cloyne, Ontario

Getting Out

My ninety-three-year-old father tells a story of the very
hungry thirties when he had been out of steady work due to
a broken leg suffered in an accident in the woods. My young
brother was admitted to the Banff Mineral Hospital[38] for a
tonsillectomy. My parents received a phone call to say my
brother would not be released from the hospital until they paid
$100. I can remember my mother crying, wondering what they
were going to do. A loan was arranged at a time when $100 was
a fortune, to obtain his release.

Nellie M. Wright – Duncan, British Columbia

Mother fed any tramp that came to the door, if she had any
food at all. The young men would get off a freight train before it
came into the Danforth station in Toronto and walk down
through the Main and Gerrard area and arrive at Mother's as if by
magic. One lad asked if there was any work he could do for
Mother.

"There's plenty of work," said Mother, "but I've no money to
pay you. Have you had breakfast?"

"I haven't eaten for two days."

Mother fed him some toast and tea left over from breakfast.
She ferreted out his story. He had come from Scotland in the
spring to work on a farm. He had worked hard for the whole
season and saved $67. In November, as the farmer didn't need
him any longer, he came to the city in search of work. Within a
week he had become ill. His landlady shuffled him and his
pneumonia off to the hospital. On discharge, they took all his
remaining savings to pay the hospital bill. He had no place to go,

no relatives in all Canada, and no money in his pocket.

"He was only a few years older than our Miles," I heard Mother telling Daddy. "Oh Arthur, what becomes of these poor boys? This one was a nice lad, too, and didn't want to be beholden to anyone. If we'd had a spare bed, I'd have put him up until he was feeling better."

Grace Rosamond – Toronto, Ontario

She had had a total hysterectomy the day before and despite the clerk's protests was discharging herself

In the summer of 1968 I entered the Royal Victoria Hospital in Montreal for a tonsillectomy. Seated next to me as I registered was a young woman who was discharging herself from the hospital.

There were no privacy dividers between us so we could easily hear the other's conversation with the staff. I had Blue Cross;[39] the lady beside me didn't have any insurance and was a recent immigrant. She had had a total hysterectomy the day before and despite the clerk's protests was discharging herself because she couldn't afford the $520-per-day fee to stay in the hospital.

To put the per diem in perspective, when I started my first full-time job that summer, I earned $320 per month.

Jean F. Milne – Vancouver, British Columbia

Shortly after I was discharged from the army I developed blood poisoning in my leg. We were living in Toronto then and I had a good-paying job as a travelling salesman. I had just cashed my paycheque and also a travel advance and had $600 in my wallet. I thought I had better check in at the hospital before I left on my business trip and when I was examined they admitted me immediately and started treatment. I had to turn in all my personal belongings, including my $600, and was informed that it would all be put in the office safe and not to worry.

When I was released they wheeled me down to the office and

gave me my envelope, which was opened, and my bill marked "paid in full." They had taken the money from my wallet. Needless to say I raised quite a stink.

Our family doctor charged $2 for a house call and I must say that doctors in those days were wonderful and did not press for payment. When the wife became pregnant he suggested that we go through the free clinic at the hospital, this was in Montreal at the Homeopathic Hospital,[40] and all we had to do was pay for the hospital room.

When it was time for her to come home she was presented with the bill with instructions that it must be paid before she could be discharged. I took the bill down to the office and informed them that I couldn't pay the whole amount but would pay them

Okay, you keep her!" and I started for the door

at the rate of $2 per week which they thought was a joke, and they would not release Mrs. Stewart until the bill was paid in full. So my answer to that was, "Okay, you keep her!" and I started for the door.

I didn't get very far and they suggested a discussion with the head man. When he realized that I was serious he signed the release form and said he would order a taxi. I said, "Forget it, we must go home on the street car," and furthermore, I would have to ride up to the hospital on my bicycle as that was the only method of transportation I could afford. We worked on Saturday morning then until one o'clock and I said that I would come straight from work every Saturday and pay my instalment. Incidentally, it was an eight-mile ride. Glad to say we eventually paid the bill in full.

H. E. Stewart – Don Mills, Ontario

After we came in 1950 to Canada, my wife needed an urgent operation. She was admitted to the old Mount Sinai Hospital in Toronto.[41] The daily hospital-bed rate was $6 at this time. She was in the hospital for about ten days and the total bill came to almost $300 including the operation, etc. At this time it was a lot of money, considering I was making $35 per week. As newcomers, we did not have $300 cash, but I was supposed to pay a good part of it in order to get my wife discharged. For a whole day I had to run around to borrow money until I had $200 together. Now I was allowed to take my wife "home."

John W. Angres – Saint Catharines, Ontario

A farm family from near Wakaw, Saskatchewan, had a very sick child. During the night the mother brought this child to the Saskatoon hospital. The next day, while I was on duty, this tearful mother came in to pay her deceased child's hospital bill. She reached into her dress in the bosom area where she had the money they got from, as she said, "the sale of one of their two cows." After paying the bill she did not have enough money to pay the funeral home for a casket and shipping charges to take the body of her deceased baby home.

This case was explained to the Canadian National Railways agent who advised if she wrapped the body in a blanket and kept the covers closed she could take her baby's body home in her arms.

The other employee in the office and I paid a taxi to take her to the train and help her board that train.

The agent advised that she wrap the baby's body in a blanket to take it home

Frances Berscheid – Calgary, Alberta

Paying Up

Doctors often had a hard time collecting their bills in the days before Medicare. They accepted payment in kind and struggled on with a lack of cash, occasionally resorting to drastic measures to collect. Early insurance plans established by doctors' associations or provinces began to help with medical costs beginning in the 1940s. Losing a lifetime's property, savings or a business to pay for medical care was a constant possibility. Many without money simply went without care, with tragic results. And those who could pay often shouldered a huge burden and paid it off over the long, long haul.

Doctors Collecting

While life was hard for the rank and file of people, doctors found it even more so. To start with, they needed to travel a great deal. On top of that, a good half of their patients failed to pay the bill. There was little they could do to collect because the patient had little or no assets.

Arthur W. Fletcher – Hythe, Alberta

We delivered three chickens ready to cook to his house each Saturday

Dr. George Whissell settled in Westlock, Alberta, early in the years of World War II. I don't know how much he charged in general, but he charged us $1 per office visit. I think house calls were the same, though I don't know for sure. (I was born in 1931.)

Dr. Whissell had ulcers, and liked chicken. In the late 1940s and early 1950s we (farmers) delivered three chickens ready to cook to his house each Saturday. I didn't have anything to do with the finances, so never collected for the chickens. I found out only years later that these deliveries were to pay for a surgery I had had in 1948. I guess the arrangement was good for him and for us.

Philip Garrison – Saint-Polycarpe, Quebec

Both my father and grandfather were doctors here so I grew up hearing stories of families and their problems paying their medical bills. Often my grandfather would be paid with fish, lobster, meat, fruits and vegetables.

Mary Louise Matheson – Halifax, Nova Scotia

My sister was ever so ailing and always in need of a doctor's care. In those days, they actually came to the house! The bill soon ran up beyond our ability to pay.

Now, this is the sore spot in my heart, and still angers me to this day: my parents agreed to pay the doctor by giving to him paintings done by my own grandfather, James Burberry (my mother's father). I can still picture these paintings as they hung on the wall as you walked up the stairs and then along the hallway. This doctor finally got them all except one or two of my grandfather's smaller works, one of which I do possess today and hang in

I can remember our unspoken anger

my home with pride. This mode of payment was, of course, at the doctor's choosing. He was well paid.

Alas! How I would have loved to have told him how wrong I felt he was to take from our home something precious and family-oriented. I can still see the three of us sisters as a picture would be taken down from its rightful place. I can remember our unspoken anger.

Irene E. Ord – Saint Thomas, Ontario

Doctors had a code whereby friends, the minister, or other doctors got free delivery of babies and perhaps other services as well. That's the way the exchange system worked.

Vivian Abbott – Rowanwood, Ontario

Paying medical bills was not a problem for us. Collecting was a big problem. But what do you say to a young man who had been a commando in Europe for five years and whose nerves were shot? He looked well, but hit the ground whenever a car backfired. He couldn't keep a job, but he named his daughter for me and for the nurse, after a home delivery. He couldn't afford a hospital either.

My husband was not practising when the provincial health plan started.

Emma Gordon – A small town, Ontario

When my wife died I had hospital bills here in Orillia or Toronto, and bills for three nurses. Dr. Rynard never chased me for his bill, not one bit. But he told me, "You'll be going to a doctor in Brechin," because Rynard still owned the practice, and he left a young doctor there in his place. And he says, "Anytime you have any spare money give it to the young doctor and get a receipt and he'll give it to me." So I did.

It wasn't a great while afterwards, I got a letter from him and he was wondering why I couldn't pay a little. So I got the receipts and I put them down in front of him. It just took his breath, because he, the young doctor, just took the money and high-tailed it.

Howard Eastcott – Orillia, Ontario

My father was a general practitioner totally committed to his patients and his Hippocratic oath, until the stress and pressures finally killed him in the fifties. When he began his practice in the twenties he charged people for their visits less than the cost of the medicines he was giving them, so aware was he of their inability to pay.

One day my father said to my mother, "Would you be willing to take over the bookkeeping?" She said something along the lines of, "I thought you'd never ask." From that day, the billing and record keeping were more efficient but still fair and humane to the patients. His concerns about their ability to pay were somehow lifted from his broad shoulders.

Jean Smith – Toronto, Ontario

Doctor's bills were so hard to pay and doctors themselves had a terrible time. Our doctor was an alcoholic and my husband's family's doctor was a drug addict. Was it that they couldn't pay their bills and raise their families or were they so devastated by the lack of care they could give their patients?

E. Clem Brown – Parksville, British Columbia

In Nova Scotia in the small Annapolis Valley village of Berwick a much-loved doctor named Bezanson practised the healing arts for many years, including the dirty thirties. He was quite innovative and was one of the first doctors to use the old-type Bombardier snow machine for transportation in the winter.

He took off his coat and gave the deliquent payer a thorough thrashing

Dr. Bezanson did not press people to pay their bills but one time during the thirties he found his practice about to collapse because of cash-flow problems. He was owed thousands of dollars but could not pay for the drugs and equipment he needed. Debtors ignored his requests for payment and one day the doctor decided to make personal visits to try to collect some money. Towards the end of a near-fruitless, frustrating day he stopped at the home of a farmer who had paid nothing for the delivery of his last six children. The farmer had a reputation as being an abusive family head. When the doctor requested some payment of the bills outstanding for many years, the farmer laughed in his face and said, "I've got no money. I guess you'll have to take it out of my hide." Dr. Bezanson did just that. He took off his coat, gave the delinquent payer a thorough thrashing and then made out a formal receipt stating, "Paid In Full."

Donald I. Shade – Petawawa, Ontario

Dr. René Coulombe settled in Sainte-Marthe, Quebec, about 1930. I knew him starting in 1964. He never charged for office calls. I asked him one time what he did for a living. He said he charged for house calls, and also made some mark-up when he sold pills and such, from a small pharmacy he kept. When Medicare came, he was delighted. He said the amount of money he received would be somewhat higher, but what particularly pleased him was that he would no longer have to chase anyone who didn't pay.

Philip Garrison – Saint-Polycarpe, Quebec

Early Insurance

Having had a diving accident in 1949, rendering me quadriplegic at the age of nineteen years after just one year of university, I was protected by my parents from the knowledge of the cost of my three years of top-notch medical and rehabilitative services. When I was accepted at the University of Toronto's School of Social Work, in spite of innumerable problems of how I would manage my living, I left home to attend that school.

I could not be covered

At that time, in the early fifties, newspaper advertisements declared that medical insurance could be purchased from various companies without any questions asked or medical information required. I was angered by what I felt certain was blatant misrepresentation and so filled in and sent applications to several of those companies. Whenever a company set a follow-up date, I suggested a few students stay with me for the appointment to witness the charade, as I had stated my views many times to the other students living with me.

What followed was a piteous display of the salesman's total inability to disguise his horror on seeing me in a wheelchair. He knew nothing, nor did he desire to learn anything, of my general health. There were a few comments back and forth before his making it clear that, of course, I could not be covered. No matter what I said about the promises of the advertisement, he fended me off with inconsequential remarks which just fanned the air for his speedy departure.

The students were surprised and appalled. I was merely appalled.

Marilyn Noell – Toronto, Ontario

Newly married, I discovered I was pregnant. At that time it was illegal to disseminate (oops, pardon the unintentional pun) birth control information. My husband had just gone back to school to upgrade his qualifications, and we were living on savings. Shortly before he graduated, our first baby was born – $110 for the delivery and prenatal care, $20 for the anaesthetist. The salary range my husband could expect as a beginning teacher was between $1,800 and $3,600 a year, with a median of about $2,600. The janitor was paid $4,700.

I have since wondered how many mothers-to-be with similar income levels had prenatal care, and a doctor-assisted delivery. And what happened to their babies, if like mine, they were born underweight and needed special facilities? By the way, the hospital stay, at that time, was covered by our medical insurance.

The following year, when my baby was now ten months old, it was discovered that I had Hodgkin's disease. As the alternative to treatment was death before Christmas, I opted for treatment. The expected survival rate was five percent. At the end of the treatment, the bill was in excess of $10,000. An early version of OHIP[42] picked up ninety per cent of the cost, leaving us with a bill in excess of $1,000. We were still paying off debts incurred during the time my husband went back to school.

Juanita Farnsworth – Omemee, Ontario

I had the experience of having insurance through Physicians Services Inc. through my husband's job and had our children and us cared for with no financial worries when many others had no such coverage. This was 1953.

My fifth child was born in 1955 and I had varicose vein surgery three days after he was born. A week later I saw a visitor in the hospital who obviously needed varicose veins tended to much more urgently than I but she shook her head and said they couldn't afford it.

This time, I felt like one of the privileged.

Jane Cook – Cross Lake, Manitoba

In 1955, my one-and-a-half-year-old son smashed my nose with the back of his skull, while playing with my husband on our bed. I was not fully awake, but the crunch and pain were nauseating. Of course it happened on a Saturday morning, and I waited until Monday for a doctor's appointment.

We picked a doctor from the Ottawa telephone directory, without any referral. I underwent a bone-set procedure under anaesthetic, spending two nights in a local hospital. I was released with a most peculiar splint, consisting of tapes which pulled my fractures into the desired shape.

This contraption was removed in about a week, and I began a series of seven to ten repeat visits to the doctor's office. He saw me each time for about two minutes. "Uh hum! Keep massaging. See me next week." On my last visit another patient commented on all the repeat visits this doctor required, and questioned his ethics.

The same day I was presented with an account by the doctor himself, for $150, and "payment today please." I was stunned, and replied that settlement would be made upon receipt of our insurance cheque. The doctor said insurance companies only paid a pittance, and he expected settlement up front. I gave him a personal cheque for the $150 and telephoned my bank as soon as I returned home to stop payment.

We submitted the account immediately to our insurance company in Toronto. My husband received a telephone call from the insurer at work, to say we had been grossly overcharged, and should not honour the bill. Their schedule covered $15 only, leaving us with $135 owing, a great amount of money in those days. We ended up paying two-thirds of the account to avoid a lawsuit.

Connie Bailey – Ottawa, Ontario

In 1956 my husband was posted in Germany. Just prior to returning home in December 1957, I suffered a gall bladder attack which was tended to at a British military hospital in Germany. When we returned home with our one son who was born in Germany we purchased Blue Cross to cover me and our son. My husband was covered by the military.

In 1958 I had a bad attack. This was a major problem as we had not been in British Columbia for six months and therefore were not covered by the hospital plan,[43] but thought that the Blue Cross would cover the doctor's fee. A week before the operation was scheduled, British Columbia changed the residence stay to three months, so we were elated.

Our second son was born October 21, 1959. Several months later when I was visiting my doctor I found out I owed him $125 for the pregnancy which was not covered because my husband was not on the Blue Cross plan, and that I owed $500 for the gall bladder operation. That operation was not covered after all because it was a prior condition.

We were just devastated and did not have funds to pay. I offered to borrow the money, but our doctor was good enough to allow us to pay him $10 per month. It took us five years to pay off that debt. It was quite a financial burden. That debt was more than we paid for a used car. It was twenty-five percent of the value of the house we had purchased for $300 down and $25 a month in 1954.

Maureen Beardsley – Ladysmith, British Columbia

Immigrants from western Europe were used to some degree of insurance against the costs of sickness and injury, but being totally without such insurance was a concern, if not a worry, particularly during the first few years while getting established in a new country.

Freek Vrugtman – Carlisle, Ontario

I came to Canada from Britain in the fall of 1964. My bilingual English-Canadian husband got a job in Montreal with a financial journal. We settled in and started to save money to cover the birth of our second child, expected in June of 1965. Quebec had free hospitalization[44] but we had to pay the doctor for his prenatal care and the delivery. It was $200, I believe. We could just afford it.

We were not imprudent. My husband had paid into Blue Cross for the six years that he was in England, without asking for a cent back since he was covered by the British National Health Scheme. But in the confusion of packing up a household to leave, he had missed a payment. Blue Cross cut him off. They were adamant in their refusal to accept his explanation. He was reinstated eventually but the gap in coverage meant that I had become pregnant while we were not covered and therefore could not benefit from the insurance for the actual pregnancy and delivery.

Being at home, pregnant and caring for a young child, I listened to the radio a lot. The debate raged over the federal government's plan to introduce Medicare. I listened in a constant state of disbelief and plied my husband with questions and comments when he came home from work. I just could not understand how anyone could not want Medicare. I became glued to the open-line shows on this subject. I particularly remember the man who said that having a government scheme would diminish his manhood because he would no longer be providing for his family in all respects. Furthermore, in discussions with the elderly couple who lived in the ground-floor apartment, I became even more amazed. The husband was vehement in his denunciation of a public health insurance scheme, yet he agonized over whether they could afford to have both of his wife's legs operated on for serious vein blockages, or just one – and if just one, which one!

Maureen Cassidy – Ottawa, Ontario

Losing It All

If you were a farmer, paying for a serious illness could mean impossible debt and consequent loss of your farm. In one Southern Ontario district it was said that the three largest landowners were the doctor, the banker, and the lawyer. In the city, prolonged hospitalization and medical bills could mean the loss of your home.

As a result, mothers in particular often denied themselves medical care. My own mother, at a time when we were away, fell and broke her wrist. She set it herself; it healed strangely askew, but she never consented to having it properly re-set.

My own mother fell and broke her wrist. She set it herself

> B. L. Williamson – Ottawa, Ontario

One of my personal friends and her husband, unable to pay for the medical care incurred due to the still-birth of twins and an injury sustained in Holland during the Second World War, fled across the country with their two young children and all they could pack into their automobile. They wrote to their creditors promising to pay off their debts as soon as they were able. They kept their word by arranging for a relative to come from the Netherlands to care for their children when they were well enough to work, which they both did to pay the bills.

> Mildred Cleverley Holst – Delta, British Columbia

In February of 1947, my little girl, aged one year and nine months, was badly scalded by a falling kettle of boiling water. She was in the hospital for about six weeks until we had to bring her home due to lack of money.

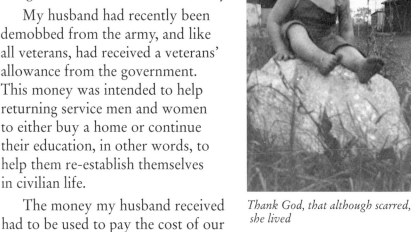

My husband had recently been demobbed from the army, and like all veterans, had received a veterans' allowance from the government. This money was intended to help returning service men and women to either buy a home or continue their education, in other words, to help them re-establish themselves in civilian life.

The money my husband received had to be used to pay the cost of our

Thank God, that although scarred, she lived

daughter's hospital care. When it was used up we had no choice but to remove her from hospital, and bring her home before she was fully healed and recovered. The VON[45] came to the house twice a week to give her saline baths and treat the burns.

Thank God, that although scarred, she lived. But I have to say that the financial setback affected us for many years.

Joan G. Davison – Lombardy, Ontario

My husband was attending the University of British Columbia under a veterans' program. We were receiving $97 a month, for one child, from the government.

My doctor charged $75 for each delivery, and gave us a $25 veteran's discount. I used to pay $5 on each of my monthly visits.

We eventually sold our home and moved into a veterans' tract, to free up capital as our family increased to four boys.

Minerva Black – Burnaby, British Columbia

My mother, a teacher, had an older woman come in to clean up the apartment once a week. This woman was old Gaspé stock and had married an Englishman who had served all his life with the British army in India. After moving to Canada, he was told his pension was cancelled. When he came down with cancer of the bowel, Anora came to mother about the cost of operations. My mother talked to a doctor friend, and was told that the practice was not to charge more than the patient could afford, which she passed on.

After the operation, and despite pleading, the full price was charged. This ended the family's self-sufficiency. When they went to the city of Montreal they were told to spend any remaining savings accountably, and they would go on the dole. The husband died, leaving a shattered family.

Jack Martin – Wakefield, Quebec

Don and I were married in June of 1960. We decided to live in an apartment for a year or so and look for a house. We had wonderful plans for our future.

In October of that same year, Don became ill and was put in the hospital. His doctors informed us that he had to have a lung removed. They operated successfully but Don would need a lot of care.

The company he was with had some medical coverage, but not all that we would need. I was working and making $45 a week. There were our savings in the bank for our house. Thank goodness for this, as the doctors told me Don needed twenty-four-hour private nursing. I had to leave three envelopes daily with $15 cash in each for the three eight-hour shifts, more a day than my take-home pay a week. I was very upset, but Don came first. Don came home Christmas Eve, and was off work one year.

Thanks to relatives, friends, my church and family, we came through that year. But we were very broke. Our dreams and hopes were smashed.

Bunny Kusey – Orillia, Ontario

When I was expecting my first baby in Rivers, Manitoba, in 1951 my husband and I were having a puzzling time about finding money to pay the doctor and the nursing home for their services. Both amounts were $50 and as my husband was a poor struggling airman, we did not have $100.

Do you have a car? Sell it!

First of all, we asked the Air Force Benevolent Fund if they would loan us the money to pay these bills. No. They asked us if we had a refrigerator. Well, yes, we had purchased it on time and felt it was a necessary thing to have and keep if one had a small child. The reply was, "Sell it!" Next question: "Do you have a car?" Yes, we had a 1935 Terraplane with the wheels welded on. "Sell it!" How was my husband to get to work and how would I get to the nursing home when the baby announced its arrival?

E. Clem Brown – Parksville, British Columbia

My story took place in Toronto in 1958. Ironically, I was involved in a fledgling business offering a service to the medical profession for processing and servicing medical claims through medical insurance carriers, on behalf of medical doctors and their patients.

These services generally applied to groups of employees who were covered for medical insurance through their employers. My company was covered by such a group plan.

However, there were many restrictions, limitations and requirements for these group contracts between the employers and the insurance companies. My employees' group was covered by a contract from Prudential of America General Insurance, a major medical group insurance carrier.

My son, who turned eighteen years of age at that time, was covered under my coverage, but there was a restriction that dependent children of subscribers were only carried to age eighteen. A few days just after his birthday, my son was hospitalized with a severe sinus infection that settled in his brain and required very serious and extensive brain surgery. There was little hope for recovery. He required twenty-four-hour nursing care at a tremendous cost of $25 per eight-hour shift (a fortune in those days).

Prudential Insurance Co. paid, gratuitously, for some minor medical expenses. The surgeon did not press me for payments, but arranged for reimbursement over a long period of time.

The first operation was for a tumour that infected his brain and there were three follow-up surgeries over a year. All the time, he required continuous nursing care.

I eventually was forced to sell my business and finally declared personal bankruptcy and was in debt for the first time in my life, for over $10,000. I lost my house equity and all my savings. There was no respite from the financial burden which had befallen us.

My son eventually recovered but was a chronic epileptic and was on a strict regimen of drugs and lived a restricted life with very frequent attacks. He passed away during an attack in his twenty-ninth year.

Harry Fields – Toronto, Ontario

No Money, No Care

I had to raise four children on one income and the fact I remember most vividly is that the doctor was the last one to get paid and at times he had to wait and wait and wait. The other thing I remember is that my children were the ones who visited the doctor mostly. My husband and I did not go unless and until we tried everything else to help ourselves in order to keep the doctor's bill down to the minimum. Mind you, it did teach us that if we ignored some aches and pains they would go away.

Olga Atkinson – Nepean, Ontario

It was 1925 and I was fifteen years old. At a scrub soccer game (we called it football in those days), I collided with another boy about my age, and as a consequence I shattered the cartilage in my left knee. My knee immediately locked and I couldn't straighten it. We had a family doctor, to whom mother and dad owed money for the delivery of the latest baby. We weren't very good payers, and I don't think he was very glad to see me in the condition I was in. He said to me, "You will outgrow it." He definitely didn't want to do anything about it. Why should he? Chances were very high that he wouldn't get paid for his work, and at the best he probably would have to wait a long time for his money, so why bother? He wanted patients who could pay for their services.

The knee would never completely straighten out, and was a little sore, but I persevered, and although it was always swelled up, and painful, I was able to get by okay.

G. O. Ryckman – Stony Mountain, Manitoba

I grew up on a farm in southwestern Ontario, the eldest of five children. The year 1919 when I was thirteen happened to be a bad year for crops. We had two teams of work horses, and dad managed to get work in the city hauling construction material on the wagons to construction sites. We were hauling brick, cement blocks and lumber.

It seemed like there were a lot of rainy days. Sometimes our clothes hadn't completely dried when we put them on the next morning. We were sleeping in a hayloft over the stable where the horses were kept, so our clothes would be hung up and dried with the temperature in the upper part of the stabling. There were no fork-lift trucks those days, so there was lots of labour, hard work.

After a couple of months I developed stiff, painful joints. Oh, that's just growing pains. No doctor was contacted due to cost. I developed rheumatic fever.

Blake Mulcaster – Hawkestone, Ontario

Thirty-five years ago, my husband's mysterious illness was finally diagnosed. He suffered from Parkinson's. At that time there were no miracle drugs. Our only hope lay in the hands of a famous surgeon who had developed a surgical procedure on the brain which promised considerable success. I can never forget the day we faced him in his office. Without looking at my husband, even before examining him, he said, "And how do you propose to pay for this surgery, Mrs. Sacks?"

And how do you propose to pay for this surgery, Mrs. Sacks?

Evelyn Sacks – Montreal, Quebec

During the forties and early fifties Perry Ronayne and his wife were having and bringing up their children in Halifax. Times were tough and there wasn't much money. Perry was working on the CNR trains and was often away for days at a time. Their second infant was born at home and seemed

Nothing could save her at this late stage

to have difficulty nursing from the beginning. The doctor didn't come to the house when they called because they still hadn't paid the bill from the birth of their first child.

As the days and weeks went by the situation did not improve. The baby would drink some milk and then throw most of it up. Advice was sought from well-meaning friends, because there was no money for the doctor's fee. All kinds of efforts were tried to help this baby. When the baby was almost two months old, Perry came home from work with enough money to take the baby to the Halifax Infirmary Hospital.[46] The paediatrician on staff that night checked the emaciated child gently.

There was a minor problem with the baby's upper digestive system, that was apparently not at all uncommon and easily fixed. But it was too late. The baby was starving to death and not even intravenous fluids could save her at this late stage. She died soon afterwards.

Mary Louise Matheson – Halifax, Nova Scotia

One story concerns a three-year-old boy in Newfoundland who lost his hearing after red measles. The parents were told by a surgeon in Montreal who could and would operate, that he could restore the child's hearing. But the cost was $2,000, in the thirties, and the family did not have the money. The child grew up deaf. He was educated at a school for the deaf in Nova Scotia, so he was deprived of his family, and his hearing.

Grace Rosamond – Toronto, Ontario

I was a single parent, found it very tough. I am a mother of four daughters. I worked all my life and I was not on welfare. My salary was not high, and with all the financial expenses to bring up my family, I found it difficult to pay doctors' fees. As a result I let my own health deteriorate. For example, I was not able to pay for a specialist when I was experiencing ear problems. I now have Meniere's disease and I often wonder, when I had and I still have tinnitus, had I gone to a specialist, would I be well today? I remember making the appointment and having to cancel it because I just could not afford it.

Ten years ago I suppose I would not have written this letter because of pride. I used to keep all my worries to myself. Pride is good in its place.

Florence McIntyre – Riverview, New Brunswick

The following true story took place when I was a small child and it made a lasting impression. The event took place just prior to World War II, when rural Canadians were reeling from the Depression.

A young neighbour lady was diagnosed as suffering from cancer. In that era there were no treatments or cures, it was known as the death sentence. The victims usually spent their remaining weeks in the hospital with large doses of morphine being administered. This treatment dulled the pain but did not alleviate it. With no help for medical bills this usually meant the victim's family lost or had to sell everything to pay the outstanding medical bills.

This young woman refused to leave her home and as the disease progressed the pain was excruciating. When her husband went out to work she had him lock the door, so no one could come in answer to her screams of pain. Her screaming and suffering lasted for two months, but she never gave in. Her whole being was dedicated to saving her husband and family the debt of medical care that would have ruined him.

The pain was excruciating

Donalda Pilling – Brandon, Manitoba

Paying: The Long Haul

My mother was terminally ill for several years during the Depression.

At the end of the dry and Depression years on the prairie we harvested a fair-to-good crop, the first in many years. I hauled our wheat to the local grain elevator using six horses. One team was a big team of Belgians, weighing close to a ton apiece. The other four I used in a four-horse hitch as they were smaller.

Our granary was located about five miles from our local elevator. I made three trips a day hauling out over 1,600 bushels of number one wheat, which weighed sixty-two pounds to the bushel. The price per bushel was ridiculously low, and we never knew from one load to the next what price it would bring. The three-decked wagon box held eighty-two bushels per load and the grain had to be shovelled by hand with a hand scoop shovel.

I rode the wagon thirty miles a day for six days. I changed outfits of horses every other day so that one outfit made one trip a day and the other team made two trips a day. Using a pick and shovel, I dug two long trenches for the back wheels of the wagon so it would be lower to shovel the grain from the granary into the wagon box. I dug the trench deeper every third trip. Every morning I was up very early to feed, clean and harness the horses, then back to the house for breakfast as I had to be on the road early to be at the elevator when it opened, then back to the granary to load the second load. Dad would have dinner ready for me so I would eat dinner in a hurry, then change outfits of horses, and head for town again. I'd unload at the elevator, back again to the granary to load and haul the third load of the day. The daylight hours were short so I loaded the next morning's load by lantern light. I greased the wagon every other day to keep it from excessive wear. This routine continued until the granary was empty.

When I had finished hauling the wheat, I handed Dad the cash-grain tickets and the next morning he left for Kerrobert, Saskatchewan, a distance of forty miles, to pay what bills he could from our mother's illness. He arrived back home well after dinner time and he asked me to get him a lunch as he was hungry, and he had had no dinner.

I said, "Dad, why have you had no dinner? I gave you cash tickets for a car-load of wheat." Dad replied, "Because I had no money left, the doctor and hospital bills took it all." There wasn't a cent left to pay Bick's Drug Store for the drugs, and it was paid much later when my twin brother and I came home from serving in World War II.

Ellis Jamieson – Major, Saskatchewan

I rode the wagon thirty miles a day for six days

A dear old aunt of mine had her fifth and last child during the depths of the Depression. They were eking out a very hard living on a prairie farm where the crops seemed to fail every year. In those days you paid for any and all medical services that you received. They were not able to pay the small fee the local country doctor charged for a delivery (I believe it was $15), so the debt remained unpaid, and over the years seemed to become forgotten.

However, this had always bothered my aunt, so when she became seventy,[47] and received her first old age pension cheque, she endorsed it and sent it to the doctor with a short apologetic note for all the years it had gone unpaid.

Duncan Mitchell – Consort, Alberta

My mother, often ill, had to see the doctor every month for high blood pressure, and she also had a lot of eczema. It was enough to drive you crazy with worry. Often she'd fail to take her medicine or fail to go and see the doctor through lack of money. Luckily, my father's health was good. He worked as a low-paid labourer. He took any job offered to him and never lacked for work. In spite of that, life was hard. He never had a car. To save money, he walked to work and back, morning and night. He took his lunch. There was no possibility of going to a restaurant or going on a trip, or even of having a beer. His money all went for his family. Mother would make new things for us out of something old.

I was ten and my sister was eight when my mother gave birth to her third child. Listening very hard, I was worried that the doctor didn't want to deliver her at home. She had to go to the hospital for her life was in danger. They had to figure out, from their skimpy budget, what that would cost. In those days you didn't go into debt to buy luxuries, but for medical care.

Micheline Mercier – Montmagny, Quebec

Hilda Pearce, volunteer, Canadian Cancer Society. Cancer "hasn't been the winner"

When I was six-months pregnant in 1935 I was diagnosed with breast cancer. I had a radical mastectomy which left me with a very disabled arm. Much blood was needed after surgery and blood donors were a professional group called upon by the hospital when their special type was needed. The cost to the patient was $25. When your salary is $100 per month, $25 is a very large amount of money. Every Friday afternoon the hospital bill for the previous week was delivered to the patient, adding to the already overwhelming stress, but stress was not a great concern in those days. When a friend became aware that we had paid for some transfusions he came forward and insisted that he be called for future transfusions – a great blessing.

January 1939, I gave birth to a second child after a very trying eight months. The greatest concern of course was the possible return of the cancer. Fortunately, it waited for a couple of years. However, we once again had the blood-donor problem and our friend had moved to another province.

After the birth of our second baby there was a breast abscess, a rectal problem, a bacterial infection, a third pregnancy which the doctor said he couldn't go through even if I thought I could, a second mastectomy, a tumour removed from the uterus, a hysterectomy, and cancer in my leg.

All these happened before Blue Cross Group Insurance came to Montreal.[48] I am sure we were the first family to sign up. We had long ago had to start paying the hospital by the month.

Hilda Pearce – Ottawa, Ontario

In 1922 one of my brothers became sick with appendicitis. The doctor had a nurse come and later my brother had to go to Winnipeg for an operation. In 1927, the year before the polio epidemic spread across the country, my brother and I came down with it. When my spine started to bend the doctor sent me to Winnipeg and I was

One-third of the cattle had to be sold to pay for the operation and hospital

operated on. One-third of the cattle had to be sold to pay for the operation and hospital. Then came the Depression.

In 1937 I was married. My husband had gone to British Columbia and found work. We had three children and lots of medical bills. We were quarantined for scarlet fever and while I was sick I had to have my appendix out. I had not had any of the childhood sicknesses and therefore had them all, even had to be in isolation again when my third child was born because I had chicken pox. Medical bills came every paycheque, taking away any opportunity to save or make life easier.

Stefania Morris – White Rock, British Columbia

This is not my story, it is my parents'. In June 1944, their fourteen-year-old son contracted the deadly tularaemia virus while skinning an infected rabbit. He was the third eldest of seven children, the youngest being three at the time. They lived on a poor mixed farm. Times were tough at the best of times.

Floyd lay in a coma in hospital for three months, passing away August 23, 1944. At times, three special nurses were needed around the clock. I don't know the dollar figures, but think on it. Specialists were called in, an expense above and beyond the regular doctor. And the hospital! A private room was needed because of the nature of the disease. Imagine those dollars! And no insurance or help in any form. Donors donated blood or that would have been $25 a shot. Then after all that, the funeral expenses.

Cream checks,[49] their only income, couldn't begin to cover the bills, so Dad hired out to work in a logging camp in late October. One month later he suffered a broken leg from an errant log. A friend carried him out on his back to the camp. He spent nine months in hospital, but fortunately, was covered by Workmen's Compensation[50]. The morning he was discharged, Mother was taken in with severe blood poisoning in her hand and arm. Dad didn't know Mother was coming in because there were no telephones to speak of yet. In midsummer the remaining son was hospitalized for blood poisoning in his leg.

I don't remember the size of the cream checks, but they were stretched beyond endurance. And only the young children to milk the cows.

Doreen Thomeus – Entwistle, Alberta

On April 22, 1934, here in Saskatoon, Saskatchewan, my mother, Marie Cole, died in Saskatoon City Hospital. I was fourteen years old, my brother six years. Mother had colitis and had been in hospital for some time after being in bed, at home, for weeks. As I remember she had been ill from the New Year. Despite blood transfusions and intravenous (rare in those days, sixty years ago), mother died, aged thirty-six.

The last few days of her life my father arranged for special nurses day and night. It was the Depression and nurses were glad of a job. My father had a job, with Canada Customs and Revenue Department. Father's salary was not great, but we felt fortunate as so many were unemployed and on relief.

Then the bills came in. There was no bank account to draw on, just the salary to spread between nurses, hospital and funeral parlour.

My Dad went to the bank to arrange a loan in order to pay the two nurses who were dependent on their salaries. He visited the funeral directors to arrange so-much-a-month payments. Then the hospital bill arrived. I remember thinking they must have a large typewriter carriage since the paper was the size of wallpaper! Every aspirin, every sanitary pad, every single thing was itemized. I don't know if I ever heard the amounts. We just knew they were enormous.

When my father re-married a couple of years later, he was still paying off the bills for mother's illness and death. Needless to say, money was scarce in his new family.

Leone M. Donaldson – Saskatoon, Saskatchewan

I was born June 12, 1927, the first child of a gardener and a housewife. There were three more children. In May 1938 we were visited upon by red measles. My mother and the four of us succumbed to its raging. On June 26 my closest brother had surgery on both mastoid bones. He was a patient for six weeks.

In November 1938, my father was admitted to Toronto General Hospital for hernia surgery. Complications led to kidney infection and it was six weeks before he was discharged.

On May 1, 1939, suffering from chronic mastoiditis, I was operated on and there was no healing until I also had a tonsillectomy. I was discharged on my twelfth birthday, the third six-week hospital stay for us.

Now, we were lucky enough not to have doctor bills from these episodes but the hospital bills had to be paid.

The summer of 1938 my mother started taking in laundry from the summer tourists. We lived on Lake Simcoe, a summer resort. She could have asked the township for assistance, but vowed to never ask for help as long as her strong back and resolute wit held together.

I do not know how long it took, but she did pay off that responsibility after a matter of years and her struggle coloured all our lives.

It was not all negative as we saw how she reached her goal by hard work and determination.

Jane Cook – Cross Lake, Manitoba

I was discharged from the services in late 1945. My wife, a previous Wren,[51] had been discharged in the spring of 1945, medically unfit. She had had a nervous breakdown, and the only way to have her discharged, according to the navy doctors, was to become pregnant.

In November we were blessed with a lovely baby girl, and in January 1946 I brought them up to my old home from Montreal.

In that spring my wife got so she could not breathe, and an operation was done in a Barrie hospital. The upshot of it was I had to pay the hospital and the surgeon's fee to the tune of $250. In that year alone I only made $750 as I was just starting up business with my father, painting and paperhanging.

M. A. Boyce – Saint Catharines, Ontario

Just over fifty-five years ago, my mother was operated on for, I think, ovarian cancer. She was to die from her cancer two years later.

After she had been in Women's College Hospital[52] for a week, we went to visit her after supper and found her crying almost inconsolably. Some idiot in the business office had left her bill for her surgery and first week on her bedside table. My parents' savings of twenty-two years were gone.

I'm not sure how Dad swung it, but her care was paid for

without a ripple that a thirteen-to fourteen-year-old could see. Of course, Dad carried two jobs, and I worked Friday nights and Saturdays delivering groceries on my bike.

These things were not considered unusual. In fact, we thought ourselves rather well off.

Some idiot in the business office had left her bill on her bedside table

Keith McCrea – Smiths Falls, Ontario

My parents, Jack and Bess Timmerman, lived in Malartic, Quebec, a gold-mining town, from 1946 to 1952. My father worked underground in one of the three mines there. Like most of their neighbours, my parents were young and looking for work and a place to live, after the war. Everyone had small children.

In August 1950, Dad had been having chest pains for a few days but the company doctor could find nothing wrong and sent him back to work. Eventually the pains got so violent that Dad had to leave his shift and go home. The next day, he collapsed and had to be rushed to hospital in Val d'Or where a doctor told my mother that Dad had recently suffered a heart attack. From my mother's account of Dad's symptoms and the

Dad had been having chest pains for a few days

massive haemorrhaging in Dad's heart tissue, the doctor figured that a clot had hit an artery in the heart a week earlier, down in the mine. For days after that, Dad had unknowingly over-worked and strained his already battered heart, giving it no chance to recover. The doctor could not understand why the mine doctor had not recognized the symptoms; "Any competent G.P. would."

My mother didn't leave the hospital for a week. They said that if Dad was going to have another attack, it would most likely occur within forty-eight hours. After that, he had a better chance of surviving, closer to fifty per cent. At the time, Dad was thirty-seven years old.

My mother, then thirty-five years old, found herself marooned in Malartic, Quebec, six hundred miles north of Ottawa, with winter coming on, the sole support of a desperately ill husband and two little girls. She had $60 in the bank that was already earmarked for the house mortgage and the monthly expenses. The basic hospital rate was $10 a day. Dad had to be in an oxygen tent that cost another $10 a day. He was to be in that tent for fifty days, in all. The first week in the hospital had cost an additional $24 a day for round-the-clock nurses in intensive care. There were charges for x-rays and medicines mounting up. Sixty dollars in the bank? She was looking at expenses of $60 a day! How would she manage? She couldn't even let herself think of the long run, that Jack would likely never work again.

Friends thought that there might be some money from the mine coming and maybe from the Quebec Workmen's Compensation Board but the mine doctor was already distancing himself from her and, anyway, any possible compensation was months of paperwork away.

Mom managed to talk herself into a job at the office of one of the other mines, despite her two-finger approach to a typewriter and her lack of any stenographic training, because of the fact that there were very few women job-seekers in the area. Most women were busy producing families. On the job she had to learn quickly. She was the sole stenographic staff for the manager, assistant manager and five department heads of a mine which employed two hundred men! In the evenings after her exhausting days, Mom made the trip to Val d'Or to visit Dad at the hospital and try to hide her worry about the bills. She was earning $40 a week.

As Dad gradually regained his strength, he took on the task of the correspondence with the mine and with the compensation board. The compensation board had taken the position that Dad's heart attack did not qualify as "a condition due to an accident or an industrial illness." The mine management was pleased to concur. If Mr. Timmerman had "over-exerted" himself on the job, it was none of the mine's affair. Management did not seem concerned that the mine's own physician had examined Dad after the initial attack and sent him back down in the shaft to perform hard labour.

The letters went back and forth. My parents were never successful in their claim and never got any compensation either from the compensation board or from the mine. Whatever the legal battle, the point is that this couple got no help.

My father died two years later when another clot hit his heart. My mother continued, in her personal life and in her career, to promote the cause of a Medicare system for Canadians. She was most impressed with the efforts of T.C. Douglas, the CCF premier of Saskatchewan, to bring Medicare into his province. Mom voted CCF and then NDP for the rest of her life.[53]

Robin Lunn – Picton, Ontario

My first son was born in 1946, before any health coverage was available in Ontario. My husband was in the air force making $2.40 a day and I received $37 a month as his spouse. The motto of the air force was: "last in, last out."[54] As a result, he wasn't discharged until late that year at the age of twenty-two.

I had planned to work as I was a nurse but a difficult pregnancy and delivery prevented that. Our baby was born with health problems and the costs mounted.

We were fortunate that the hospital I graduated from gave us a break in costs and I went home to my parents to save money. My mother-in-law was in a nursing home in a distant city as the result of a stroke and my father-in-law died suddenly just before the baby was born. As an only child, my husband was now responsible for his mother's expenses also. How could we make ends meet? Since we had no assets, no one would lend us money, not even the finance companies at twenty-four per cent. My husband was given a compassionate discharge to deal with all his problems. Although he had been working on a university degree before the war, he took the only job he could find, working in a clothing store.

After a few weeks in hospital, the baby and I came home with the assistance of a nurse. The baby was being fed with an eye dropper every hour because of a feeding problem. The medical bills continued and we could only pay a small part of them each pay day.

Slowly things began to improve. My husband got a better job and we got our own place. When my little boy was thirteen months old, I was in a car accident and spent

A drunk driver ploughed into me

the following year in a body cast. A drunk driver ploughed into me and in those days insurance did not cover anyone who was drunk.[55] I spent a month in hospital and then went home. My husband sold the old car we had, to pay the hospital bill. A housekeeper was required to care for our son, who still had eating problems, and for me, who could do little for myself. We always had food on the table but there were no extras.

I was supposed to go to the hospital for physiotherapy every day after the cast was removed, but, after three weeks I was told I couldn't have any more treatments until my bill was paid. I couldn't bear to tell my husband and instead, I told him they said I could quit the daily trips.

As a nurse, I saw many cases worse than ours. Many families lost everything when a family member became seriously ill, and many family doctors had to write off debts. The terrible pressure put on my husband has had a lasting effect as he worries about the future as we get older and more vulnerable.

It took many years and many more crises to get our medical bills paid. My husband used to say, "Every time you think you're getting somewhere the ass falls out of your pants."

Jane Leitch – Toronto, Ontario

We were a young married couple. My husband had returned home in 1945 after serving five years overseas. We had a baby boy born January 22, 1947. Everything that could go wrong, did. He was born premature, four pounds, by Caesarean section. He was a very sickly baby for the first six months, and went from one hospital to another. We were insulted, harassed. They all wanted the money immediately. The Hospital for Sick Children even threatened to keep the baby until we paid. My mother went with us and with her credit background, she was able to make arrangements for us to pay the bill. Our only debts were for doctors and hospitals, but if your debts went into the Credit Bureau, it black-listed you from borrowing any further money.

My husband would get a job and they would garnishee his wages, so he would be fired. When your wages were garnisheed you automatically were fired.[56] We finally had to sell everything we had and move in with my mother-in-law. She took care of the baby so we could go hundreds of miles away to work in tobacco so we could pay off all our medical bills and get a fresh start.

Margaret Veillette – Saint Catharines, Ontario

May 17, 1952, our first son, Bruce, was born. At this time I was informed by my doctor, Dr. L. Murray, that before I could bring my wife and child home I must pay the anaesthetist and the hospital bills.

This held true for daughter number one, 1954, and daughter number two, 1958.

The last child born caused complications with my wife, Pauline, and a repair procedure was done to correct the situation.

Dr. King of Weston performed the surgery, cost $300. I had no money to pay so I arranged to pay him whatever I could afford until I paid him off.

This was a financial burden that we did not need, but there was no help. I found part-time work and put in eighty to ninety hours a week working. When my wife recovered she found a job to help out and we paid for our own babysitter.

The fifties were tough lean years and no fancy laws to help us out. Things seemed hopeless at times but we survived.

Lloyd Attridge – Coldwater, Ontario

It is not just the paying of medical bills that one must deal with, but rather the depressing feelings one gets as the efforts to go forward have you in a position of losing ground or, at best, just treading water.

Very early in our married life (first year), we had our first child, Sharon. Soon after her birth she became quite ill and we were soon informed that Sharon had a very serious congenital heart condition, and indeed these were the days before Medicare. These were also the days when not a great deal could be done for

these children, especially those like Sharon. What really took
place then was many doctor visits, drug store visits and hospital
visits, and our expenses soared. At that time I was employed as
a machinist at the Halifax shipyards, and my wife soldiered as
a wife, mother and an untrained nurse. In addition to this, my
wife needed me at home during my off hours, but that was not
to be. Because of the mounting medical bills I had to go from
an eight-hour day to the night shift, consisting of twelve hours,
and if I could work a weekend I would do just that, which meant
working twelve straight shifts at twelve hours each. While I was
doing that my wife pressed on caring for a very sick child.

With this workload we would split my pay in half. The
first half paid our living expenses and the second half was
divided between the doctors, the drug stores and the Children's
Hospital.[57] But we were not able to even tread water.

In 1949 I wrote to Dr. Gordon Murray in Toronto. He was
one of the best congenital heart surgeons in the world. I asked
him up front what he would charge to see Sharon. The reply I
received from Dr. Murray was to be in Toronto at a certain date.

We mustered funds as best we could and even though I do not
belong to the Masonic Lodge, they, along with the shipyards, said
they would assist if we couldn't make it with the money we
managed.

It was impossible for my wife to go at this time so I was
forced to lose precious time from work. My first conversation
with Dr. Murray made me realize what Medicare in our country
would be like. He brought up the money question I had
mentioned in my letter to him. He informed me that he would
never deny a child surgery; "If you can pay, that's fine,
and if you can't pay, that's fine also." I was astonished; this
world-famous surgeon was offering me Medicare. He couldn't do
anything for Sharon, but for all the tests and attention
he said, "No charge." Because of advancements he invited us back
the following year. My wife went this time. He was still unable to
help Sharon, but again, "No charge."

My wife and I decided we should try to manage a car, which
would make it easier to get to doctors, hospitals and get Sharon

out on her better days. We had the car three months and medical bills were mounting. We decided that if Sharon had to go back to hospital one more time the car must go. You see, Sharon would be in hospital for a month at a time. It wasn't long when the car had to go. It wasn't the car as such, but rather how much easier it was for all concerned. By this time my wife and I owed the medical profession over $3,000. We were very much in debt.

Around this time, Sharon went to hospital and was there for a month. When she was well enough to come home I made my usual trip to the hospital office to find out how much the bill would be, which I couldn't pay right then. The lady looked me in the eye and said, "Mr. Baigent, you owe us nothing because we now have Medicare." My wife and I were overjoyed and we worked away at paying off our $3,000 of past medical bills.

Mr. Baigent, you owe us nothing because we now have Medicare

George W. Baigent – Halifax, Nova Scotia

Conclusions

Canadians who remember life before
Medicare draw their own conclusions about
the years before and after universal public
health care. Page numbers refer to stories,
if included earlier, that led them to these
conclusions.

It's good to remind this generation who grew up on Medicare that the bad old days aren't any further away than the Beatles.

Jean F. Milne – Vancouver, British Columbia
Page 55

Anecdotes teach like nothing else, and we need reminding of those vicious Bad Old Days!

Jack Martin – Wakefield, Quebec
Page 73

We are being told, with increasing frequency, that our medical system is threatened, particularly with respect to senior citizens. To those of us who are old enough to remember the era preceding Medicare this is extremely alarming. I can personally remember families, my own included, who experienced hardships due to lack of medical coverage.

Surely thousands of Canadians faced similar hardships prior to Medicare. It is without question one of our most needed benefits. I am hopeful that our medical professionals, our politicians and Canadians generally will have the will to curb the over-use and abuse that jeopardize it.

Wes Snider – Orillia, Ontario

I am very deeply disturbed by Ralph Klein's unadulterated attack on publicly funded health care and social programmes in Alberta. The Medicare system ensures that people never have to sign over open-ended mortgages on their homes, businesses or farms to the hospital prior to being admitted for proper medical treatment.

I would have liked to have met my grandfather; if there had been a national Medicare system in the dirty thirties, perhaps I might have.

Rod Trentham – Red Deer, Alberta
Pages 46-47

I remember the time before the health insurance system was set up. It's left its mark on me. I wouldn't want my grandchildren to live through those frightful times with its money worries.

When we're forced to go into debt to save the life of one we love, or simply to give him the care his state of health requires, and we can't afford to, it's very hard on your morale, and difficult to live through.

For my parents and for my curious little ears, it was such a relief when health insurance came into effect. What torment, what anguish was spared us!

I'm a daughter who's not forgotten those dark days.

Micheline Mercier – Montmagny, Quebec
Page 82

I look back to the years before Medicare and think of the hard life, not just of the sickness but also of the haunting worry of the medical bills that were always with us. People suffered and delayed getting help, often causing serious problems or death. There never were any checkups or preventative medicine.

There never has been or will ever be a more important thing in Canada than Medicare.

Stefania Morris – White Rock, British Columbia
Pages 19, 84

Thank God for our Medicare today. Too bad we didn't have it years ago.

Mrs. Melnyk – Winnipeg, Manitoba
Page 42

We have been very thankful for Medicare. My youngest son had open heart surgery three times since the 1970s.

Minerva Black – Burnaby, British Columbia
Page 72

Without any doubt whatever, there are many in the same position as my wife and I were but at least they are blessed with Medicare. We never complained about Medicare taxes, we never complained when these taxes had to be increased and we explained to others who did complain why we pay the tax and why we need and must keep the program. Let Canada know how important Medicare remains to Canadians.

George W. Baigent – Halifax, Nova Scotia
Pages 92-94

In those years the elderly were not as healthy, nor did they live as long or as comfortably, in health, as they do today.

After Medicare, you could slowly see the rise in the number and the lifespan of older people with a better health status.

Louise James – Cloyne, Ontario
Page 53

If I had to have paid for all my medical care in these last years, I would not own my own house now, and I do not want to burden a nursing home as I get older, and so my daughter has her instructions to leave me in my own home to the end of my days.

M. A. Boyce – Saint Catharines, Ontario
Pages 25, 87

For over thirty years, the seniors of Canada contributed and paid into health care to protect themselves and their children. It gave us a secure feeling to know we could depend on this buffer against hard times. We believed we were responsible citizens paying our taxes toward Medicare and other social services.

Mildred Fox-Baker – Carleton Place, Ontario

May our present government not take away our benefits. Let them consider that they were appointed by all the people, the poor, as well as the rich.

Florence McIntyre – Riverview, New Brunswick
Page 79

Millions of people died an early death because to go for medical care meant certain loss of home and belongings.

Come on Canada, get with it. The little people are the backbone of the nation. Start treating us with respect and give us what we are taxed and pay for.

Donalda Pilling – Brandon, Manitoba
Page 79

I feel strongly that Canadian people should be aware of the pitfalls of allowing our governments to erode our cherished Medicare.

I am thoroughly convinced that if we had Medicare in 1925 my quality of life for the past seventy years would have been much better, and I would not need a knee replacement now.

We must not allow the politicians to take our Medicare. Our grandchildren need it, Canada needs it.

G. O. Ryckman – Stony Mountain, Manitoba
Page 76

I am a healthy person, and except for brief visits to emergency for treatment of minor mishaps, I seldom needed to use the Medicare system. However, two years ago I discovered a lump in my breast. I still cannot believe the speed in which the mammogram, the doctor's consultation, the biopsy, and finally the radical mastectomy were carried out; three short weeks from the discovery of the growth to the operation. All the worry one has when the word cancer is uttered was not made worse by the terrible fear of not being able to have an immediate operation through lack of money.

If I were living in the United States, I would either have delayed the operation, probably with fatal results, or I would have had to sell or mortgage my country home where I am enjoying my retirement after forty-five years in the workforce.

I expect as fewer people are left who remember life before Medicare, it will become increasingly easier for any government to cut, slash and change our health programme, and what then? It was so difficult to achieve this "insurance against worry." It will not be easy to ever bring it back once it is lost.

Jacqueline Morris Reimer – Stittsville, Ontario
Page 43

Every day I thank God for Medicare. Remember Stanley Knowles and others who fought hard for it.

Frank Johnson – Winnipeg, Manitoba

I am appalled that the Americans, with all the wonderful things of which they justifiably brag, have not found a solution for the massive financial burden that illness places on people.

Philip Garrison – Saint-Polycarpe, Quebec
Pages 61, 65

The deductibles and extra charges involved in stateside private health insurance will wipe out modest life savings in the majority of families.

I am frequently asked about differences I see between Canadians and Americans. One big difference is that Canadians cannot conceive of not having health care, and many say that they have never seen a doctor's bill. Another difference is a term used stateside in their giant private industry, "uninsurable," a term almost unknown to Canadians in relation to their health care, where universal health care is a right.

Along with uninsurable comes "unemployable," as employers do not want to put their private health plans, written by private insurance companies, in jeopardy by hiring someone with a pre-existing condition. This is another whole subject in itself, which includes humiliation, loss of self-esteem and financial disaster.

Lest we forget: the health care system in place here has problems, yes, but is a system that is the envy and a hallmark of the world. And believe you me, it must be guarded and defended as there is a giant out there that is ready, willing, and able to attack and dismantle it in a New York minute. It's called the Private Insurance Industry.

Les Funk – Etobicoke, Ontario

I hope that the Canadian social conscience stays alive and well, and with it, our commitment to Medicare.

Apart from the social responsibility angle to Medicare there is also the financial. It is much cheaper to collect than private insurance. The administrative costs of the government scheme are a fraction of those of private schemes. We get more from our dollar to pay the doctor.

I hope that we try to improve our Medicare scheme in Canada. Please, let's not abandon it or eat away at it with user fees.

Maureen Cassidy – Ottawa, Ontario
Page 70

If I had a way to make Canadians listen, I would tell them how important our medical system is. Don't abuse it in any way. Do what you can on your own. Save our Medicare wherever possible. You never know when you and your family may need it. Cherish what we have. Until it happens to you, you'll never know how important it is. Wake up Canadians! Work for what we need for our families. It won't come on a silver platter and it sure can't stay in place without our help.

Bunny Kusey – Orillia, Ontario
Pages 26-27, 73

Canadians do not have free health care. Canada does have a medical insurance system for which every Canadian pays premiums.

Perhaps the most important feature of Medicare is its universality. At present Canadians can go anywhere in Canada or outside the country safe in the knowledge that they can obtain medical treatment if needed. User fees, a popular suggestion these days, would sound the death knell of Medicare.

Far from feeling guilty about passing on a health care system for which Canada is the envy of every other country in the world, I hope the younger generation is smart enough to appreciate the marvellous system they will inherit. There is not one thing wrong with Medicare that cannot be corrected.

W. H. Mowat – Wolfville, Nova Scotia

I feel that we could cut back by having health care provided by medics and nurse practitioners.

Helen Hansen – Willowdale, Ontario

I am foursquare behind universal medical coverage, with a single-tiered system. I think that we could possibly improve on what we have by emphasizing preventative medicine, healthy lifestyles, etc., and having community-based centres for routine medical care – pregnancies, flu shots and such – perhaps even putting in a day-care wing for frail seniors who need care, to give respite to their families. Then hospitals could be reserved for severe trauma and situations requiring extraordinary medical attention.

Juanita Farnsworth – Omemee, Ontario
Page 67

We don't want a "cash register" health care program. We should have everyone treated on an equal basis and we should pay our health care insurance according to our means.

Health care comes before sports, tourism, paved roads, world cruises, etc., etc.

Arthur W. Fletcher – Hythe, Alberta
Pages 1-2, 39, 61

My father and grandfather were both doctors. My father experienced both what it was like before and after Medicare and had strong opinions on how much more fair the new Medicare system was.

Mary Louise Matheson – Halifax, Nova Scotia
Pages 61, 78

One of the blessings of our current system is that doctors can count on payment. They can also spell each other at night and on weekends, or to take vacations which they can afford.

At the same time, there are no second-class patients. We can all go to the doctor without hesitation, knowing that he will be paid for our treatment.

The doctors we have known and loved in the past would be saddened that in some medical circles money and self-importance seem to have come to the fore these days.

Mary Albright – Elora, Ontario

It would be wonderful if, in the spirit of compromise, we could develop a modified program that would both guarantee doctors a salary commensurate with their years of training and also guarantee the same level of basic health care to all Canadians. I get annoyed when doctors claim absolute freedom to run their practices like a business. The people paying the bills, that is to say the provincial government and indirectly its citizens, must have a right to set levels of service, salaries, etc. Even in a democratic society like ours no one is absolutely free. If the doctors don't like the setup they are free to negotiate better terms, and if unacceptable leave for greener pastures.

Recipients also have to realize that if something is not done to control runaway costs, Medicare such as we have enjoyed, to the envy of many nations, will disappear. There is no one group entirely to blame for the current situation and all will have to share in the solution. Personally I would like Medicare to be geared to income and to become a clearly defined section of our income tax returns instead of the cost coming out of general revenue. That way revenue would be clearly identified and services and costs adjusted accordingly on an annual basis.

Doctors tend to make an issue of the claimed loss of freedom resulting from Medicare. Actually Medicare gives them an assured income with the government assuming the role of bill collector. A doctor would have to grossly mishandle his funds to end up other than well-off at retirement. It was not always this way.

Donald I. Shade – Petawawa, Ontario
Page 64

I hope your project will point out to the population that living without OHIP was not easy. These days when there are so many more people without jobs and the prescription drugs being so very expensive, should we lose OHIP, life would be back to the way it was during the hard thirties and the doctors would not be getting paid again as before.

Olga Atkinson – Nepean, Ontario
Page 76

The major change, as I see it, is that money becoming available through health insurance, later Medicare, and including hospital insurance, has made it possible for enormous advances in diagnosis and treatment. People no longer crave simple coverage for acute care, but expect a continuum of care: preventative, acute, specialized, rehabilitative, and long-term maintenance care, as well as chronic and home care. We expect inoculations to prevent illness, laboratory and ancillary services to diagnose, and appropriate medications and medical aids.

Admittedly, some of these services were available before Medicare, but not so readily, and only to a favoured few as a right through some personal entitlement of fortunate financial position.

Most patients in need received commendable care from the physicians, hospital and clinics they attended. Many suffered sorely. Some incurred large bills which they were unable to meet. They could then be ruthlessly pursued by debt-collection agencies to whom their doctors had sold their overdue accounts. There are still those harbouring great bitterness and fear of the medical profession based on memories of the hounding they and their families endured.

Our health care delivery system has grown more sophisticated and comprehensive, and consequently more expensive.

The increased life-expectancy of those with extremely severe disabilities and chronic illnesses, and the prolonging of life of the seriously and terminally ill, have been heroically achieved. These people and their families cannot be abandoned to struggle to try to meet costs for service and care on which we as a society have made them dependent.

In fact, through Medicare, all health-care providers, from physicians and surgeons to all kinds of laboratory services, have been able to participate in and develop a very sophisticated system which few could now hope to pay for other than through universal coverage being available at reasonable cost.

Change, it is true, is the only constant. We must endeavour to make changes wisely and not for short-term political gains.

Mildred Cleverley Holst – Delta, British Columbia
Pages 52, 71

We should put our energies into making sure our present health system is reorganized to the best advantage for all. My experience in the U.S.A. has made me appreciate our health care system. When I worked as a volunteer for a crisis line there (1986 to 1987), I was appalled at the lack of service for those in need. The occasional sad story that was publicized got community response, but mostly, those in trouble suffered. I tried to talk to other volunteers about this, thinking that because they were volunteers they'd be concerned. The answer I got was that any other system would raise taxes. They weren't willing to risk that. Their attitude was definitely that each must look out for himself. Even their answers to requests were set down in black and white. They made fun of those that called several times and just expected the set answers to apply. If they didn't – too bad.

We have had a caring system which we must work to preserve. Because of financial concerns we could evolve, and are evolving in some respects, into a mechanistic, less compassionate one. Our society as a whole is less concerned with the individual. Perhaps OHIP is a reflection of this.

Marea Lemke – Etobicoke, Ontario
Pages 21, 52

Please, powers that be, don't inflict a tragedy like this on anyone. The pioneers built the country, each succeeding generation has contributed. Everyone pays taxes in one form or another.

Our grandson was born with multiple birth defects, and is handicapped. Don't take a reasonably decent future out of his realm. His medical expenses are high. And countless thousands more are like him. No one knows what the future holds for us or ours.

Doreen Thomeus – Entwistle, Alberta
Pages 84-85

The universal way is the fair way.

Jane Cook – Cross Lake, Manitoba
Pages 67, 86

I do hope that you will be able to tell all Canadians that the Medicare we all fought for has to continue so we don't have the problems we all had prior to Medicare.

Maureen Beardsley – Ladysmith, British Columbia
Page 69

The advent of Medicare gave my mother the one worry-free period of her adult life, a miraculous reprieve.

Medicare has done more, much more than the provision of medical service for this country; it has transformed it from a rather cold, hard, negative society to the very pleasant one that we have been privileged to enjoy for the past few decades.

The dismantling of Medicare may mean more than the loss of medical help. It may signal our return to the hard old ways of the thirties and forties.

B.L. Williamson – Ottawa, Ontario
Pages 20, 71

APPENDICES

APPENDIX A

A Thumbnail History of Medicine*

1947 Saskatchewan's CCF government implements
public health insurance for hospitals.

1948 Mackenzie King's Liberal government passes the
National Health Grants Programme – mainly used
to build hospitals.

1957 St. Laurent's Liberal government passes the Hospital
Insurance and Diagnostic Services Act.

1962 Saskatchewan's CCF/NDP government implements
the Medical Care Insurance Act on July 1, and 90 per cent
of the province's doctors stage a three-week strike.

1966 Pearson's Liberal government passes the National Medical
Care Insurance Act (Medicare), implemented in 1968.

1971 All provinces in Canada are fully participating in Medicare.

1977 Trudeau's Liberal government and the provinces negotiate
the Established Programs Financing Act (EPF), replacing
fifty-fifty cost sharing for health care with per capita
"block grants" to the provinces. Federal funding under
EPF is supposed to grow at the same rate as the Gross
National Product.

1983 Trudeau's Liberal government imposes anti-inflation measures on the post-secondary education portion of the EPF grant. This lowers the over-all base on which future EPF growth is calculated.

1984 Trudeau's Liberal government passes the Canada Health Act, which sets out penalties for provinces that allow hospital user fees and physician extra-billing.

1986 Mulroney's Conservative government changes the growth formula for EPF – now it is tied to GNP minus two per cent.

1990 Mulroney's Conservative government passes Bill C-69, freezing EPF for three years, after which future EPF growth will be based on GNP minus three per cent.

1991 Mulroney's Conservative government passes Bill C-20, which freezes EPF growth for an additional two years – making a five-year freeze in total – before the new growth formula (GNP minus three percent) comes into effect. Also, C-20 makes it possible for Ottawa to withhold any federal transfer payments from provinces in breach of the Canada Health Act.

1995 Chretien's Liberal government passes Bill C-76, which joins the funding for social services under the Canada Assistance Plan (CAP) with the funding for health care and post-secondary education under EPF in a new block transfer, the Canadian Health and Social Transfer (CHST). Total Federal cash contributions are planned to be cut by 20 per cent over three years.

*Reprinted, with an addition by the authors, from *Strong Medicine: How to Save Canada's Health Care System*, by Michael Rachlis, M.D. and Carol Kushner (Toronto: HarperCollins Publishers Ltd., 1994), Table 2.1, 31, with kind permission of the authors.

APPENDIX B
Principles of the Canada Health Act

T he Canadian Health Coalition* is calling for a
new approach to health care, consistent with the
reaffirmation and enhancement of the five principles of
Medicare stated in the Canada Health Act, 1984.

Reforms to the health care system should strengthen,
not undermine, these important principles:

1. Universality

Which requires that 100 per cent of the residents of a province
be entitled to insured services on uniform terms and conditions.

2. Accessibility

Which requires that provincial health care plans provide
insured health services on uniform terms and conditions and
must not impede or prevent reasonable access to those
services by any means.

3. Comprehensiveness

Which requires all medically necessary health care services
provided by physicians or in hospitals to be covered by
provincial health care plans.

4. Portability

Which applies host-province rates to health care services
provided elsewhere in Canada and establishes national standards
for out-of-country benefits.

5. Public Administration

Which provides for a public authority appointed or designated by and responsible to the provincial government through regular audits to administer the insurance plan without profit.

Reforms should be based on our growing understanding of the social and economic determinants of health, including income, nutrition, education, housing and environment, rather than on an uncritical reliance on technology. They should make health care more democratic, empower Canadians to take more control of, and responsibility for, their individual, family and community health. They should also ensure integrated services for children, persons with disabilities, and seniors, consistent with maintaining the maximum quality of life for both patients and care-givers.

*This statement of the principles of the Canadian Health Act comes from the Canadian Health Coalition, 2841 Riverside Dr., Ottawa, Ont., K1V 8X7, at telephone 613-521-3400, or facsimile 613-521-4655, which has worked since 1979 to preserve Medicare in Canada. Membership is made up of groups representing women, senior citizens and health care providers, along with churches, trade unions and anti-poverty groups.

Notes

Chapter 1. Home Medicine

1. *The Cumulative Book Index* 1928-1932 refers to a *People's Home Library*, compiled by R. C. Barnum, published by R.C. Barnum Co., Cleveland, Ohio in 1926 containing three volumes: Book 1, The People's Home Medicine Book, by T. Ritter; Book 2, The People's Home Recipe Book, by Alice G. Kirk; and Book 3, The People's Home Stock Book, by W. C. Fair. Another volume "with the same general title-page," possibly the 1917 version described in this anecdote, is also noted. It included Health Nursing and Prevention of Disease, by Blanche Swainhardt, as a substitute Book 3.

2. Sick Kids' Hospital refers to The Hospital for Sick Children, Toronto, Ont., opened in a rented house March 1, 1875, by a committee of ladies headed by Elizabeth McMaster, with the purpose of offering free care to any who could not afford to pay. The first patients came in April, 1875. The hospital continued to offer free outpatient care until universal public health insurance was established in 1969. Archives, The Hospital for Sick Children, 555 University Ave., Toronto, Ont., M5G 1X8. The ability of patients to pay was sometimes questioned. "In 1895, 536 of 597 inpatients paid nothing and 4,321 patients were treated free at the dispensary. Although [hospital] trustees believed half of the free patients should be able to pay...further investigation was carried out by George C. Patterson who personally visited 75 of the 200 cases [under scrutiny] and...was astonished to witness the extent of the poverty and distress that existed especially at the end of the winter. He reported that the homes were for the most part clean and tidy but destitute of all comforts including heat. Many of the poverty-striken were widows or single female heads of family whose husbands had left them.... As a result of these more careful inquiries, certificates were issued to those who were to receive free service and all others were expected to pay. [Chairman, Board of Trustess, John Ross] Robertson could

assure the readers of his annual reports that 'the greatest care is
exercised to see that only those who are absolutely unable to pay'
receive medical care free (*Annual Report, 1899, 7*)." Diane Gilday,
"The Fouding and First Quarter Century of Management of the
Hospital for Sick Children," M.A. thesis, University of Toronto,
Jan. 1995.

3. Tommy (Thomas Clement) Douglas (1904-1986) was a social
democrat, premier of Saskatchewan from 1944 until 1961. He
championed public health care. See Lewis H. Thomas, ed.,
The Making of a Socialist: The Recollections of T. C. Douglas
(Edmonton: University of Alberta Press, 1982), and notes 16, 53.
However, the notion that Douglas might have favoured
midwifery as a profession appears to be erroneous. The Statues
of Saskatchewan (1905) stipulate that only qualified physicians
can practice surgery, medicine and midwifery. The inclusion
of the latter may be unique to Saskatchewan, although the act
was not enforced until after the Second World War because
of the scarcity of medical practitioners, according to Yvonne
Hansen, "Midwifery in Saskatchewan in 1920-1950: The First
Culture," Briarpatch, 9 (2): 14-18. The Midwives Association
of Saskatchewan, 226 7th St., E., Saskatoon, Sask., S7H 0X1,
confirms that training for midwives was never offered in
Saskatchewan. Native midwives were widespread, but non-
native midwives came to Saskatchewan from England and
Scandinavian countries where training was offered (about 1850-
1930). No formal training in midwifery is offered currently in
Saskatchewan. Ontario offers a bachelor degree in midwifery,
and is the only province recognizing midwifery as a profession.
Alberta offers an M.A. in midwifery, and has allowed district
nurses to act as midwives from 1919 (see note 10). British
Columbia is in the process of setting up a programme, and
Quebec trains Inuit women as midwives. For more on the
history of midwifery, and the displacement of well-educated
midwives by doctors, see Brian Burtch, *Trials of Labour: The
Re-Emergence of Midwifery* (Montreal: McGill-Queen's
University Press, 1994), 77, 79. Source: Josée Gabrielle Lavoie,
Lavoie, Sprague & Associates, Shellbrook, Sask.

4. Municipal and county seats had a responsibility to help the indigent population, and could be applied to for assistance with health care bills until public health insurance was put in place. (See Appendix A for a brief history of Medicare.) The responsibility of municipalities to care for those who could not sustain themselves in cases where churches or other charities failed to provide for them, influenced by British poor laws, dates back to pre-Confederation times. Miriam Stewart et al, *Community Health Nursing in Canada* (Toronto: Gage Educational Publishing Co., 1985), 34.

5. Mastoiditis, an inflammation of the middle ear and sinuses, was a fairly common complication of scarlet fever, measles, and ear, nose and throat infections in the days before sulpha drugs and antibiotics, available since World War II, were on hand to treat it.

6. Ross Memorial Hospital, Lindsay, Ont., est. 1902. Dates for the establishment of hospitals, unless stated otherwise, are taken from Canadian Hospital Association, *Guide to Canadian Health Care Facilities*, 1994-1995, vol. 2 (Ottawa: CHA Press, 1994).

Chapter 2. Community Care

7. A full cord of wood, piled, measures 8 ft. x 4 ft. x 4 ft. In 1995, a cord of wood costs about $160, which is 80 times the 1936 price of $2 a cord. The family debt equalling 200 cords of wood in 1936 would be equivalent to $32,000 today.

8. "The world-wide epidemic of Spanish influenza in 1918, attacking one-sixth of the Canadian population and killing approximately 30,000 people, caused untold suffering and anxiety and dramatically revealed Canada's unco-ordinated and scarce health service." Stewart, *Community Health Nursing*, 18.

9. The Alzheimer Society of Canada was formed in 1978, the first of its kind, to provide family support, education and awareness,

and to support research. It later became the model for the
Alzheimer Disease and Related Disorders Association in the
United States. Source: The Alzheimer Society of Canada, 1320
Yonge St., Suite 201, Toronto, Ont., M4T 1X2.

10. Well-baby clinics were a feature of public health nursing.
Stewart notes that divisions of public health nursing were formed
within the structure of provincial and municipal health depart-
ments with various responsibilities and at various times in
different provinces, beginning as early as 1916 in Manitoba. Soon
after observing Manitoba's scheme of providing public health
nursing services to rural communities, Alberta developed a plan
for an official district nursing service. (See story by Fletcher, 1,
"after a while a health nurse was available.") In 1919, Alberta gave
official sanction to its district nurses in remote areas to act as
midwives, and British Columbia developed district health centres,
using a staff of public health nurses. The role of the public health
nurse with emphasis upon health teaching, case findings and
preventative care in a variety of community settings brought to
the foreground the issues of education for public health nursing
and a deeper issue, whether public health nursing was a specialty
or an integral part of all nursing. For a discussion of the development of public health nursing, see Stewart, *Community Health
Nursing*, 22-25.

11. Physicians' Services Incorporated (PSI) commenced operation
in November 1947 and soon became the largest prepaid medical
care plan in Canada. PSI was sponsored by the Ontario Medical
Association and supported about 8,000 practising physicians in
the Province of Ontario. These participating physicians agreed to
allow the Corporation to prorate their medical fees in order to
meet administrative expenses and provide the reserves required
by law. In September 1969, PSI ceased operation because of the
implementation of what is now the Ontario Health Insurance
Plan. Funds remaining in the general reserve after meeting all
obligations to subscribers and physicians were used to establish
a charitable foundation for activities in the health field.
"Physicians' Services Incorporated Foundation 1993 Annual

Report," Information Services, The Canadian Life and Health Insurance Association, 1 Queen St. E., 17th Floor, Toronto, Ont., M5C 2X9.

Associated Medical Services, Incorporated (AMS) began in 1937 under the direction of Dr. Jason A. Hannah, who developed a successful prepaid medical care plan that accumulated a sizeable monetary reserve. When Ontario introduced universal health care in 1969, AMS acted as an agent for the new plan on a non-profit basis until 1972 and continued as a carrier for its subscribers. By 1975, the AMS reserve had reached approximately $14 million. In 1976 AMS was recognized as a registered charity, and established the Hannah Institute for the History of Medicine. "Associated Medical Services, Incorporated/Hannah Institute for the History of Medicine 1991-1993 Report," Information Services, The Canadian Life and Health Insurance Association.

12. Slocan, B.C., "incorporated as a city in 1901, reverted to the status of a village in 1958." 1,001 *British Columbia Place Names*, 3d ed. (Vancouver: Discovery Press, 1969), 159. Slocan was known as Slocan City before 1897. *Encyclopedia Canadiana*, 1977, s.v. "Slocan." See note 13.

13."Early in the 1890s there were silver and lead finds at Slocan Lake where famous mines like the Slocan Star and instant settlements like Sandon, Slocan City and New Denver came into existence." George Woodcock, *British Columbia: A History of the Province* (Vancouver: Douglas & McIntyre, 1990), 161. Collective methods for providing health services related initially to the employees of industry, mainly because the services of physicians were otherwise unlikely to be available in the locality, eg., on the frontiers, in the railways, the mines and the forests. H. E. MacDermot, *One Hundred Years of Medicine in Canada* (Toronto: McClelland and Stewart, 1967), 82-83.

14. The Toronto General Hospital, Toronto, Ont., founded in 1829, merged in 1986 with The Toronto Western Hospital, founded 1896, to form The Toronto Hospital. Source: The Toronto Hospital administration.

15. The Red Cross Hospital, Cobalt, Ont., under the authority of the Mine Managers' Association, treated miners for accidents and disease. Hundreds of miners were treated during the 1910 typhoid epidemic and stayed on to convalesce. At one point, more than 100 nurses worked under the direction of the hospital. There was also a district nursing service attached to the hospital, later supported by the town. *Cobalt Daily Nugget*, January 8, 1910, vol. 1, no. 49.

16. Tommy Douglas announced a plan for Medicare in Saskatchewan in 1959, but it was not put in place until 1962 because of the strong opposition of the province's doctors. Douglas thought of Medicare long before this, however. He suffered from osteomyelitis as a boy, and after a long period of hospitalization, he remembers, "the doctors attending me told my parents that the leg would have to be amputated and they were given some time to decide whether or not to agree to the amputation. During that period in Children's Hospital in Winnipeg, about 1913 or 1914, Dr. R. J. Smith, a very famous orthopaedic surgeon, was going through the wards with a group of students and became interested in my case. He interviewed my parents and told them that he was prepared to take over, providing they would allow the students to observe. As a result of several operations, he saved my leg. I always felt a great debt of gratitude to him; but it left me with this feeling that if I hadn't been so fortunate as to have this doctor offer me his services gratis, I would probably have lost my leg.... I felt that no boy should have to depend either for his leg or his life upon the ability of his parents to raise enough money to bring a first-class surgeon to his bedside. And I think it was out of this experience, not at the moment consciously, but through the years, I came to believe that health services ought not to have a price-tag on them, and that people should be able to get whatever health services they required irrespective of their individual capacity to pay." Lewis H. Thomas, ed., *The Making of a Socialist*, 7. See notes 3, 53.

17. Pontiac County Co-operative Medical Services operated from about 1948 until 1990 in the Pontiac, north of Ottawa in western Quebec. Source: Community contacts, Shawville, Que.

18. McLeod presents a couple of versions of the origins of public health care in Saskatchewan in this anecdote. In 1914, the rural municipality of Sarnia, Sask., without legislative authority, levied for the purpose of offering its doctor a salary to induce him to stay. In 1916, the Rural Municipality Act of Saskatchewan was amended by the provincial legislature to grant authority to rural municipal councils to levy for this purpose. Malcolm G. Taylor, *Health Insurance and Canadian Public Policy*, 2d ed. (Kingston and Montreal: McGill-Queen's University Press, 1987), 70. The Rural Municipality Act was significantly overhauled in 1917 and the new new Rural Municipality Act contained the same provision. *Statues of Saskatchewan*, ch. 14, 1917. Matt Anderson was reeve of the rural municipality of McKillop, Sask., first elected in 1924. It seems unlikely that the Rural Municipality Act of 1917, or part of it, would have been popularly named after him, according to staff at the Archives, The Province of Saskatchewan. These Archives hold Anderson's personal papers. He is regarded as one of the fathers of Medicare in Saskatchewan, having taken a trip to Norway in 1919 to obtain information about health care policy and other social policy developments in Europe.

19. Kindersley Union Hospital, Kindersley, Sask., est. 1925.

Chapter 3. Hospitals

20. Probably what is now The Queen Elizabeth II Hospital, Grande Prairie, Alta., est. 1914, a unit of the Grande Prairie General and Auxiliary Hospital and Nursing Home, District No. 14.

21. Saskatoon City Hospital, Saskatoon, Sask., est. 1909.

22. Saint Joseph's Hospital, Sudbury, Ont., est. 1896. Replaced by Laurentian Hospital in 1975. Sources: OHA and Laurentian Hospital Administration.

23. Probably the Centre hospitalier Hôtel Dieu d'Amos, Amos, Que., est. 1930.

24. A form of municipal assistance. See above, note 4.

25. The Norfolk General Hospital, Simcoe, Ont., est. 1925.

26. The Royal Victoria Hospital, Montreal, Que., a teaching hospital since it was established in 1894. Source: Royal Victoria Hospital administration.

27. The Ottawa Civic Hospital, Ottawa, Ont., est. 1924.

28. The Hôpital Maisonneuve, Montreal, est. 1954, merged in 1971 with the Hôpital St-Joseph de Rosemont (est. 1950 as Le Sanitorium St-Joseph) to form the Hôpital Maisonneuve-Rosemont. Source: Hôpital Maisonneuve-Rosemont administration.

29. The Drumheller Regional Health Complex, Drumheller, Alta., began as a municipal hospital in 1918. St. Mary's Health Care Centre, Trochu, Alta., was established in 1909.

30. The Regina General Hospital, Regina, Sask., est. 1907.

31. The University of Saskatchewan was founded in 1909 and operates at several locations across the province. *Canadian Encyclopedia*, 2d ed., s.v. "Saskatchewan."

32. Saint Paul's Hospital (Grey Nuns) of Saskatoon, Sask., est. 1907.

33. Hospitals varied in their fees and procedures for blood collection. The Canadian Red Cross Society did not enter the scene until 1940, when it held a blood donor clinic in Toronto. "Organized for the sole purpose of collecting blood for war casualties, [this clinic] soon became the first of many. During the Second World War, more than 2.5 million bottles of blood were processed and sent overseas to aid injured civilians and

Canadian forces personnel. When peace returned, Red Cross was asked to continue to collect blood for civilian needs. Before that time, families and friends of patients were asked by [some] hospitals to donate twice the blood used by the patient, but supply fell short of demand. To obtain a more secure blood supply, Dr. William Stuart Stanbury pioneered the development of a national blood service to be managed by Red Cross. As a result, the Vancouver "Blood Depot" opened its doors in 1947, collecting blood from donor clinics and distributing it to hospitals free of charge…. Today there are 17 blood centres across Canada." "Over 50 years of Service & counting," Blood Services, The Canadian Red Cross Society, 67 College St., Toronto, Ont., M5G 2M1. See Pearce, 83.

34. The Queen Elizabeth Hospital of Montreal, Que., est. 1894. See note 40.

35. Another form of municipal assistance. See above, note 4, and stories by Hopkins, 41, Melnyk, 42, and Abbott, 53.

36. The Government of Ontario established the Ontario Medical Services Insurance Plan (OMSIP) in 1966, which provided insurance on a voluntary basis for physicians' services. It was offered to persons inadequately covered by private insurance plans, to pensioners and the self-employed, and assistance was available for those who needed help to pay the premiums. It continued until Ontario joined the national plan under the Medical Care Act of Canada in 1969. "Health Insurance – Ontario." Information Services, The Canadian Life and Health Insurance Association.

37. St. Michael's Hospital, Toronto, Ont., est. 1892.

38. The Banff Mineral Springs Hospital, Banff, Alta., est. 1930.

39. Hospital care pre-payment group plans on the American Blue Cross model with hospital association sponsorship appeared in Manitoba in 1939; Ontario, 1941, Quebec, 1942; Manitoba, 1943; British Columbia, 1943; and Alberta, 1948. The Ontario, Quebec and Manitoba plans also eventually offered medical benefits. *Encyclopedia Canadiana*, 1977, s.v. "Insurance, Health." The non-profit Blue Cross movement began in the United States in the 1930s. In 1952, the Canadian Council of Blue Cross Plans joined all of the Blue Cross Plans operating in each province, except Saskatchewan, to offer national coverage, with administrative offices located at the headquarters of the Ontario Hospital Association in Toronto. By 1950, Blue Cross plans protected 35 million North Americans. Ontario Hospital Association, Communications Services, *Sixty Years of Service, A History of the Ontario Hospital Association*, 1924-1984 (Toronto: Ontario Hospital Association, 1984.), 8-10, 18, 21.

40. The Homeopathic Hospital, Montreal, Que., founded in 1894 to treat patients by homeopathic methods, was renamed the Queen Elizabeth Hospital in 1951, by which time it was following more mainstream medical practices. Source: Osler Library, McGill University, Montreal, Que.

41. The "old Mount Sinai Hospital" in Toronto in 1950 would have been the hospital's first location on Yorkville Ave. It was founded by an active group of women from Toronto's Jewish community in 1923 to serve the community and provide a strong teaching centre for young Jewish doctors. In 1953 the new Mount Sinai Hospital opened its doors at 550 University Ave., moving to its present location in 1973. "Celebrating 70 Years of Health Care, Mount Sinai Then and Now," Mount Sinai Hospital, 600 University Ave., Toronto, Ont. M5G 1X5.

Chapter 4. Paying Up

42. The "early version of OHIP" was the Ontario Health Services Insurance Plan (OHSIP), which provided health care coverage to all Ontario citizens as required by the Medical Care Act of Canada in 1969, co-ordinating existing insurance services,

including private plans and OMSIP (See note 36). In 1972 the Ontario Health Insurance Plan (OHIP) combined all of the hospital and medical plans under a single public administration. "Health Insurance – Ontario," Information Services, The Canadian Life and Health Insurance Association, Toronto.

43. In 1957 the federal government promised to share half the costs of hospital insurance plans operated by provinces to cover all their citizens, under the Hospital Insurance and Diagnostic Services Act. On July 1, 1958, Newfoundland, Manitoba, Saskatchewan, Alberta and British Columbia had programs in operation eligible for federal cost sharing. Nova Scotia, New Brunswick and Ontario introduced their programs Jan. 1, 1959. Prince Edward Island began on Oct. 1, 1959 and Quebec's plan began Jan. 1, 1961, eleven and a half years after Saskatchewan had pioneered such a plan alone. Taylor, *Health Insurance and Canadian Public Policy,* 2d ed., 234.

44. Quebec provided coverage under the Hospital Insurance and Diagnostic Services Act from Jan. 1, 1961. See above, note 43.

45. The Victorian Order of Nurses (VON) is a national, non-profit community health organization that provides nursing care in the home, especially for the elderly and chronically ill. Created in 1897 through the work of Lady Aberdeen, wife of the Governor General of Canada from 1894-1898, its initial aims were to provide visiting nursing services to districts without access to medical facilities and to establish cottage hospitals in isolated areas. *Canadian Encyclopedia,* 2d ed., s.v. "Victorian Order of Nurses."

46. The Halifax Infirmary Hospital, est. 1933, in 1987 amalgamated with the Camp Hill Hospital (which was founded in 1916 and treated casualties of World War I and the Halifax explosion) to form the Camp Hill Medical Centre. In 1995 this will merge with three other facilities to become the Queen Elizabeth II Health Sciences Centre. Source: Camp Hill Medical Centre administration.

47. Old-Age Security (OAS) was introduced in 1952 through the National Department of Health and Welfare. The elderly were defined initially as persons over 70. Andrew Armitage, *Social Welfare in Canada* (Toronto: McClelland and Stewart, 1975), 128. In 1966 the age to receive OAS was dropped to 65.

48. A Blue Cross hospital plan was introduced in Quebec in 1942. See note 39.

49. Cream checks were bonuses issued by dairies to farmers for cream delivered separated from the milk.

50. The provision of medical aid to injured workmen in industry was initiated in Ontario in 1914 by the enactment of the Workmen's Compensation Act. Similar legislation quickly followed in other provinces. MacDermot, *History of Medicine in Canada*, 83.

51. Wren was a nickname in World War II for a member of the WRCNS, Women's Royal Canadian Naval Service.

52. Women's College Hospital, Toronto, Ont., est. 1913.

53. Thomas Clement Douglas was a long-time member of the Co-operative Commonwealth Federation (CCF), a party devoted to democratic socialism founded in 1932. Douglas first ran as a CCF candidate in the 1934 Saskatchewan election. In 1935 he was elected federally as a CCF member, and left the House of Commons in 1944 to lead the CCF to provincial victory in Saskatchewan, introducing Medicare in Saskatchewan in 1959. Medicare was established there in 1962, following a strike by Saskatchewan doctors. In 1961, Douglas re-entered federal politics, becoming the leader of the New Democratic Party (NDP), the successor to the CCF. He led the NDP until 1971, remaining in Parliament until 1979. The CCF formed a government only in Saskatchewan, but its policies on Medicare, old age pensions, unemployment insurance and family allowances have been adopted by other governments. *Canadian Encyclopedia,*

2d ed., s.v. "Douglas, Thomas Clement," "Co-operative Commonwealth Federation." See notes 3, 16.

54. The slogans "Last in, last out" or "First in, first out" described the order of discharge from the Canadian Armed Forces adopted at the close of World War II. Those who had signed up last were, in theory, discharged last.

55. Until about 1972, when the statutory conditions of automobile insurance acts were changed, there was no insurance for damage caused by impaired drivers. Insured persons violated their policies by driving drunk, and insurance companies took no responsibility for their actions. Source: The Insurance Bureau of Canada, 181 University Ave., 13th Floor, Toronto, Ont., M5H 3M7.

56. Section 9 of the Employment Standards Act, Province of Ontario, legislated against this in 1978, stating: "No employer shall dismiss or suspend an employee on the ground that garnishment proceedings are or may be taken against the employee."

57. The Children's Hospital, Halifax, N.S., opened in 1909, and became The Izaak Walton Killam Hospital in 1970. Source: IWK administration.

References

Armitage, Andrew. *Social Welfare in Canada: Ideals and Realities.* Toronto: McClelland and Stewart, 1975.

Blumqvist, Åke and Brown, David M., eds. *Limits to Care: Reforming Canada's Health System in an Age of Restraint.* C. D. Howe Institute, Policy Study 20. Ottawa: Renouf Publishing Co. Ltd., 1994

Crichton, Anne, and David Hsu, with Stella Tsang. *Canada's Health Care System: Its Fundings and Organization.* Ottawa: Canadian Hospital Association Press, 1990.

Decter, Michael B. *Healing Medicare: Managing Health System Change and the Canadian Way.* Toronto: McGilligan Books, 1994.

Gibbon, John Murray. *The Victorian Order of Nurses 50th Anniversary: 1847-1947.* Montreal: Southam Press, 1947.

Gifford, C. G. *Canada's Fighting Seniors.* Toronto: James Lorimer and Company, 1990.

Lyall, Ernie. *An Arctic Man: Sixty-five Years in Canada's North.* Edmonton: Hurtig Publishers, 1979.

MacDermot, H. E., M.D. *One Hundred Years of Medicine in Canada (1867-1967).* Under the auspices of The Canadian Medical Association. Toronto: McClelland and Stewart, 1967.

Ontario Hospital Association, Communications Services. *Sixty Years of Service: A History of the Ontario Hospital Association, 1924-1984.* Toronto: Ontario Hospital Association, 1984.

Rachlis, Michael, M.D., and Carol Kushner. *Second Opinion: What's Wrong with Canada's Health Care System and How to Fix it.* Toronto: Harper & Collins, 1989.
—. *Strong Medicine: How to Save Canada's Health Care System.* Toronto: HarperCollins Publishers Ltd., 1994.

Rosenbluth, Vera. *Keeping Family Stories Alive: A Creative Guide to Taping Your Family Life & Love.* Vancouver: Hartley & Marks, Publishers, 1990.

Stewart, Miriam, Jean Innes, Sarah Searl, and Carol Smillie, eds. *Community Health Nursing in Canada.* Toronto: Gage Educational Publishing Company, 1985.

Taylor, Malcolm G. *Health Insurance and Canadian Public Policy: The Seven Decisions That Created the Canadian Health Insurance System and Their Outcomes.* 2d ed. The Institute of Public Administration of Canada. Kingston and Montreal: McGill – Queen's University Press, 1987.

Thomas, Lewis H., ed. *The Making of a Socialist: The Recollections of T. C. Douglas.* Edmonton: University of Alberta Press, 1982.

Whelan, Ed and Pemrose Whelan. *Touched by Tommy: Stories of hope and humour about Canada's most loved political leader, T. C. Douglas.* Regina: Whelan Publications, 1990.

Index of Contributors

*Numerals refer to the pages
where contributors' anecdotes appear.*

ABBOTT, VIVIAN, M.D., of Rowanwood, Ont., 53, 62.

ALBRIGHT, MARY, of Elora, Ont., 106-107.
*Born Mary Carter in Toronto, 1919. Had four children in
three different countries between 1941 and 1961. Now has
four grandchildren. In New York, wrote child-care articles
for national magazines, chaired a committee that founded
an international nursery school. In Geneva, supervisor for
Amnesty International, also member of committee promoting
breastfeeding.*

ANGRES, JOHN W., of St. Catharines, Ont., 57.

ATKINSON, OLGA, of Nepean, Ont., 76, 108.

ATTRIDGE, LLOYD, of Coldwater, Ont., 92.

BAIGENT, GEORGE W., of Halifax, N.S., 92-94, 101.
*Born 1924, Melville Cove, N.S. Worked as machinist apprentice.
Married schoolteacher, Eleanor. Family dedicated to basic survival
of Sharon, through expert nursing care and 84-hour weeks for
George, plus correspondence courses to upgrade his education.
Retired 1979 as Supervisor, Engineered Standards.*

BAILEY, CONNIE, of Ottawa, Ont., 68.

BARR, BEULAH M., of Hillsdale, Ont., 11-13.

BEARDSLEY, MAUREEN, of Ladysmith, B.C., 69, 110.

*Born 1936 in Kamloops, B.C. Married Leslie Beardsley,
1955. Has three children and three grandchildren. Retired
1989 because of heart problems from career as claims adjuster.
Involved in art world on Vancouver Island, particularly
Tozan Cultural Society. Building wood-fired kiln on the
grounds of Malaspina University College.*

BERSCHEID, FRANCES, B. ED., of Calgary, Alta., 49, 57.

BLACK, MINERVA, of Burnaby, B.C., 72, 101.

BOHMAN, JOHN, of Weston, Ont., 10.

BOYCE, M. A., of St. Catharines, Ont., 25, 87, 101.

BROWN, E. CLEM, of Parksville, B.C., 64, 74.

CADIEUX, THELMA, of Pierrefonds, Que., 50.

CASSIDY, MAUREEN, of Ottawa, Ont., 70, 104.

*Born in Lancashire, England, 1937. Married Canadian
journalist, came to Canada in 1937. Has three sons and
two grandsons. Father, a Unitarian minister. Was taught
to help people. Has expertise in in a variety of crafts.*

COOK, JANE, of Cross Lake, Man., 67, 86, 110.

COOPER, I.L., of Armstrong, B.C., 32.

DAVISON, JOAN G., of Lombardy, Ont., 72.

*Married in England in 1941 to Canadian soldier. First son born
in 1942. Husband sent to Sicily, returned to England by hospital
ship 1944. Joan sailed for Canada in 1944 with son, expecting
second child. Husband arrived in 1945. Third child born 1946.
Husband died in 1968. Widowed with three dependents and no
insurance. Joan remarried in 1977, is now retired.*

DICKSON, ROSALEEN, of Carleton Place, Ont., 34.

DONALDSON, LEONE M., of Saskatoon, Sask., 85-86.

EASTCOTT, HOWARD (1912-1995), of Orillia, Ont., 24, 63.

ELSON, ANN, of Picton, Ont., 30-31.
Married 1954 to George Elson, secondary schoolteacher at Prince Edward Collegiate Institute, Picton, Ont. Has four children and four granddaughters. 1967-1970, Dar es Salaam, Tanzania. George taught in girls' secondary school for CIDA. Returned to Picton, widowed 1979. Civic and church volunteer activities, local and national.

ETHIER, BIRGIT, of Medstead, Sask., 1, 4, 17.

FARNSWORTH, JUANITA, of Omemee, Ont., 67, 106.

FIELDS, HARRY, M.E.S., of Willowdale, Ont., 74-75.
Born in Toronto, 1912. Was customs officer, 1931-1942. Joined army, discharged in 1946. Owner Doctors' Business Bureau 1956-1971. Sales Director before retiring to get degree at York, 1985, then Masters in Environmental Studies in 1989. Activist for seniors and disabled organizations. President of B'Nai Brith, President of Associated Jewish Seniors, Man of the Year, Toronto Star, 1989.

FLETCHER, ARTHUR W., of Hythe, Alta., 1-2, 39, 61, 106.

FOSTER-CLAMPITT, V., Langley, B.C., 3.

FOX-BAKER, MILDRED, of Carleton Place, Ont., 102.

FUNK, LES, of Etobicoke, Ont., 104.

GARRISON, PHILIP, of St-Polycarpe, Que., 61, 65, 103.

GARVEY, RAY, of Vancouver, B.C., 27-28.

GORDON, EMMA, of a small town, Ont., 29-30, 62-63.

❀ ❀ ❀ ❀ ❀ ❀ ❀ ❀

Gradnitzer, Mary, R.N., B.Sc.N., Quesnel, B.C., 28-29.

Born Westport, Ont., 1938. Moved to Quesnel, B.C., in 1964. Worked as public health nurse for 20 years. Married with two children. Enjoys hiking, cross-country skiing, reading, the CBC, and talking to seniors.

Haine, Robert G., of Cranbrook, B.C., 35.

Hallman, John, of Oro, Ont., 9.

Hansen, Helen, of Willowdale, Ont., 105.

Holinaty, Elizabeth, of Edmonton, Alta., 18-19.

Born in Wakaw, Sask. Post-secondary education at University of Saskatchewan and University of Alberta. After teaching for 36 years, retired in 1991. Interested in textile arts. Now pursuing weaving, embroidery, and the study of ethnic arts.

Holst, Jacob, of Delta, B.C., 2, 5.

Holst, Mildred Cleverley, B.A. Admin., of Delta, B.C., 52, 71, 108-109.

Hopkins, Betty, of Saskatoon, Sask., 48-49.

Born 1918. Grew up on farm on the prairies through the Depression. Farmed with husband, Geoffrey, south of Conquest, Sask. Retired to Saskatoon, 1979. With her husband, interested in world affairs and social issues, such as the Crow Rate, the future of railroads, and government budget cuts.

Hopkins, Geoffrey A., of Saskatoon, Sask., 39, 41.

Born 1913. Grew up on prairie farm during Depression. Went overseas for four years in the Canadian army. Married after his return. Farmed south of Conquest, Sask. Retired to Saskatoon, 1979. With his wife, interested in world affairs and social issues, such as the Crow Rate, the future of railroads, and government budget cuts.

JAMES, LOUISE, of Cloyne, Ont., 53, 101.

JAMIESON, ELLIS, of Major, Sask., 80-81.
Age 75, veteran of WWII. Served as Amphibious Commander in Aleutian Islands, then went overseas in South Saskatchewan Regiment. Born on western prairie, has been farmer-rancher all his life. Lives with wife Doreen. Has two children and three granddaughters.

JOHNSON, FRANK, of Winnipeg, Man., 103.

KUSEY, BUNNY, of Orillia, Ont., 26-27, 73, 105.

LAAKSO, LILLIAN, of Ottawa, Ont., 39-40.

LARSON, DOROTHY OWENS, of Peterborough, Ont., 22-23.

LAVOIE, JOSÉE GABRIELLE, of Shellbrook, Sask., 40-41.
Grew up in mining towns in northern Quebec. Daughter of a Health Administrator. Her career in health has taken her to Uganda, Newfoundland, Quebec, the Northwest Territories and recently to northern Saskatchewan, where she lectures in native studies and health for the University of Saskatchewan.

LEITCH, JANE, of Etobicoke, Ont., 90-91.
Has worked with the Victorian Order of Nursing for 10 years. Spent several years as president of two major seniors' groups, the United Senior Citizens of Ontario, and the Senior Citizens Consumer Alliance for Long Term Care in Ontario.

LEMKE, MAREa, B.A., Ph.N., of Etobicoke, Ont., 21, 52, 109.
Born 1925. Wife, mother of three, two sons and one daughter. Worked in public health with City of Toronto. Taught nursing assistants, then on social work staff at Princess Margaret Hospital. Now retired.

LESTER, JEAN, of Napanee, Ont., 44.

LORENTOWICZ, GENIA, of Toronto, Ont., 44, 45.

LUNN, ROBIN, of Picton Ont., 88-90.

Born at home in Malartic, Que., 1946. Now lives in Picton, Ont., with her husband and two sons. Currently working on a novel based upon the lives of her parents.

MACDONALD, MARGARET, of Kilbride, Nfld., 32.

MACPHEE, EMILY, of Perth, Ont., 2-3, 6.

Born 1918, South Acton, Mass. Born again in a tent meeting in Kentville, N.S., Lived most of her life in the Maritimes. Retired as schoolteacher after 33 years. Participated for five years in Terry Fox run. Collects poetry. Has over 4,000 children's poems.

MARTIN, JACK, of Wakefield, Que., 73, 99.

Born in Montreal, 1931. Went to King's School, Montreal High, then art school in Montreal, Detroit, and London. Married Heide Steiner of Bremner, Germany, has four daughters. Retired from commercial art in 1988. Now painting landscapes.

MATHESON, MARY LOUISE, of Halifax, N.S., 61, 78, 106.

Born in Halifax, N.S., 1959. Father and grandfather were doctors; grew up hearing stories of families and their problems paying medical bills. Now married with two children, six and 11. She and husband work at Dalhousie University. Mary is Timetable Co-ordinator.

MAYOR, RUTH, of Winnipeg, Man., 20-21.

MCCANN, WILMA, of Orillia, Ont., 33.

MCCREA, KEITH, of Smiths Falls, Ont., 87.

MCDOWELL, WILLIAM E., of Shawville, Que., 23.

McINTYRE, FLORENCE, of Riverview, N. B., 79, 102.

Born in Charlo, N.B. Educated by nuns in Dalhousie. Was a bilingual businesswoman in Moncton, N.B. Raised four girls as a divorcée, upgraded career in Saint John. Family grown, she travelled extensively. Now disabled, enjoys gardening, reading, walking, and volunteering at the hospital.

McLEOD, THOMAS H., of Ottawa, Ont., 34-35.

MELNYK, MRS., believed to be of Winnipeg, Man., 42, 101.

MERCIER, MICHELINE, of Montmagny, Que., 82, 100.

MILNE, JEAN F., of Vancouver, B.C., 55, 99.

MITCHELL, DUNCAN, of Consort, Alta., 82.

Born in 1918. Raised on small prairie farm. Joined air force. Retired to wife's home town, Consort. Was appointed postmaster there, served for 32 years. President of Union of Postal Workers. On national Board of Canadian Postmasters and Assistants Association. Ten years on Alberta Council on Aging. Three years on Board of One Voice, the Canadian Seniors Network.

MORRIS, STEFANIA (1911-1995), of White Rock, B.C., 19, 84, 100.

Born in Interlake district, Manitoba. Experienced struggles of homestead life, the Great Depression, and a debilitating attack of polio. Married Joseph, 1937. Lived in Port Alberni and Vancouver, B.C. Two sons, one daughter. Like all Icelanders, loved knowledge, reading and writing.

MORRISON, KATHERINE, of North Bay, Ont., 25-26.

Born in Barrie, Ont. Family transferred to Kirkland Lake, Ont. Loved all sports, especially hockey. Many cultures in the community taught her respect for other values. Joined RCAF at age 18, discharged 1946. Married life spent in North Bay. Son lives in Kingston.

MOWAT, W. H., of Wolfville, N.S., 105.

MULCASTER, BLAKE, of Hawkestone, Ont., 77.

NOELL, MARILYN, of Toronto, Ont., 66.

Born 1930 in Ottawa. Diving accident on a N.B. beach rendered her quadriplegic after one year of Queen's. Combined university with rehabilitation at Lyndhurst Lodge, Toronto. Graduated Queen's, Toronto School of Social Work. Long career as caseworker with CAS, Metro Toronto, breaking down physical and social barriers. Author, Another Path to My Garden *(Toronto: Dundurn Press, 1992).*

ORD, IRENE, E., of St. Thomas, Ont., 62.

Born 1925. Has three sisters, one brother. One sister, Gladys, died of cancer, "the unspoken illness." A singer, blessed with a "fair voice." Volunteer with hospital and tutor for literacy programme. Mother of three, grandmother of three.

OSBORNE, BETTY, of Toronto, Ont., 17-18.

OWENS, E. F., of Lucky Lake, Sask., 22-23.

PEARCE, HILDA, of Ottawa, Ont., 83.

Born in England, brought to Canada 1922. Lived with grandparents after mother died. Lived with husband in Montreal, Que., until 1948, then Vancouver, B.C. Settled in Ottawa after husband died. Sixteenth year of volunteering with Canadian Cancer Society. Manages well despite pain in right arm. Cancer has plagued her since 1935, "but it hasn't been the winner," she says. Has organized a 60th anniversary service of thanksgiving.

PETERS, BETTY, of Abbotsford, B.C., 7-8.

PILLING, DONALDA, of Brandon, Man., 79, 102.

Born in 1925. Background in farming communities during the thirties and WWII. Educated in a one-room schoolhouse. Elder sister required many surgical procedures; the cost caused great strain on family's meagre financial resources, and on parents. Married at 18, raised nine children.

PITTENDRIGH, ROBERT L., of Regina, Sask., 47-48.

Born on farm north of Regina. Educated in Regina. Married a schoolteacher, had two boys. Worked for City of Regina. Involved with genealogy since 1958. One of founders of Saskatchewan Genealogy Society. Contributes to two journals. Believes every family should have a history of family health.

REIMER, JACQUELINE MORRIS, of Stittsville, Ont., 43, 103.

ROSAMOND, GRACE, of Toronto, Ont., 54-55, 78.

Born in 1921. Fourth in family. Heard rich stories of bygone days as a child. Father attended Saturday evening literary society meetings. Presently writing her mother's family history.

ROSS, AUDREY, of Orillia, Ont., 3.

RYCKMAN, G. O., of Stony Mountain, Man., 76, 102.

SACKS, EVELYN, of Montreal, Que., 77.

SENYK, NADIA A., of Ottawa, Ont., 45.

SHADE, DONALD I., of Petawawa, Ont., 64, 107.

SHELLSWELL, EMMA, of Coulson, Ont., 7.

SMITH, JEAN, M.A., M.S.W., of Toronto, Ont., 63.

Born in Toronto 1926. Graduated Victoria College, 1949, in sociology. M.A. in sociology 1950, University of Toronto. Married an English teacher and had three children. Volunteered in church and community, returned to U of T to study social work, then directed a volunteer centre. Interested in church, community, politics, and family.

SNIDER, PEGGY, of Ardtrea, Ont., 18.

Born 1925 in Uppertown, Quebec City, of family of ten. Sense of history from skiing and playing on the Plains of Abraham, close family values. Peggy is an avid gardener, quilter, and volunteer English tutor. Works with church and community.

SNIDER, WES, of Ardtrea, Ont., 99.

Born in Gananoque, Ont., 1924. Educated in Lansdowne, Ont. Joined RCAF, 1942-1945. Worked at Standard Engineering in Toronto, Marine Engines, Ross Boat Works, and 40 years at Orillia Water, Light and Power. Flew small aircraft till mid 1980s. Prize-winning bird-carver, proficient at cabinetmaking and most trades.

STEWART, H. E., of Don Mills, Ont., 55-56.

THOMEUS, DOREEN, of Entwistle, Alta., 84-85, 110.

TORONTO STAR, May 14, 1933 (Toronto Star Syndicate), 10.

TRENTHAM, ROD, of Red Deer, Alta., 46-47, 99-100.

Born and raised in Drumheller, lived in Lloydminster and Calgary, Alta. Has lived for past 18 years in Red Deer, Alta. Currently co-ordinator publicity, interpretive programmes, special events, practicum and work projects at Red Deer and District Museum.

TROICUK, TONY, of Glace Bay, N.S., 33-34.

VEILLETTE, MARGARET, of St. Catharines, Ont., 91-92.

VRUGTMAN, FREEK, of Carlisle, Ont., 69.

WILSON, HAZEL, of Edmonton, Alta., 50-51.
A pubic health nurse, born in Unity, Sask. Now Director, Alberta Council on Aging, and Chair, Issues Committee, One Voice.

WILLIAMSON, B. L., of Ottawa, Ont., 20, 71, 110.

WRIGHT, NELLIE M., of Duncan, B.C., 54.
Married 46 years. Widowed. Four children, six grandchildren, all across Canada. Hobbies are square dancing, painting in water colours, and travelling to see grandchildren.